THE UNBROKEN SONG

THE
UNBROKEN SONG

Selected Writings
of Es'kia Mphahlele

RAVAN PRESS JOHANNESBURG

Published by Ravan Press (Pty) Limited

409–416 Dunwell, 35 Jorissen Street

Braamfontein, Johannesburg 2001, South Africa

First Impression 1981

© Copyright Es'kia Mphahlele 1981

Cover Art: Gamakhulu Diniso

Design: The Graphic Equalizer

ISBN 0 86975 098 4

Printed by Creda Press (Pty) Ltd, Cape Town

ACKNOWLEDGEMENTS

A number of the stories and poems have been previously published. The following are the places and dates of first publication:

'Blind Alley', *Drum*, September 1953.

'The Suitcase', *New World Writing*, New York, 1955; *Black Orpheus*, October 1958.

'The Woman', *Purple Renoster*, Spring, 1957.

'The Woman Walks Out', *Standpunte*, VIII, 4.

'The Master of Doornvlei', *Fighting Talk*, 1957.

'Down the Quiet Street', *Drum*, January, 1956.

'The Coffee-Cart Girl', *Drum*, August, 1955, (as 'Across Down Stream').

'The Living and the Dead', *Africa South,* January 1958.

'Exile in Nigeria' was first published by *Black Orpheus* and the 'Dedication' appeared in *Voices in the Whirlwind*, MacMillan, London, 1972.

'Death', 'Somewhere' and 'Homeward Bound' were published in *New African Literature and the Arts I*, ed. Joseph Okpaku, New York, 1970.

'The Living and the Dead', 'Dinner at Eight', 'The Master of Doornvlei', 'The Woman', 'The Suitcase', 'The Woman Walks Out' and 'He and the Cat' were published or republished in *The Living and the Dead and Other Stories*, Ministry of Education, Ibadan, 1961.

The final twelve stories printed here were published or republished in *In Corner B*, East African Publishing House, Nairobi, 1967.

Though action rages without, the heart can be tuned to produce unbroken music.
— Acharya Vinoba Bhave

Contents

PREFACE: Renewal Time *viii*

STORIES: Introduction *1*

Blind Alley *4*
The Suitcase *15*
The Woman *24*
The Woman Walks Out *37*
Dinner at Eight *43*
Man Must Live *54*
The Master of Doornvlei *70*
Down the Quiet Street *83*
The Coffee-Cart Girl *93*
The Living and the Dead *102*
He and the Cat *118*
The Barber of Bariga *125*
The Ballad of Oyo *140*
A Point of Identity *153*
Grieg on a Stolen Piano *171*
In Corner B *197*
Mrs Plum *216*

POETRY: Introduction   *262*

Exile in Nigeria 1960   *264*
Death   *274*
Somewhere   *278*
Homeward Bound   *280*
Death II   *283*
Vignettes   *290*
Dedication to *Voices in the Whirlwind*   *302*
A Prayer   *304*
Fathers and Sons   *309*
A Poem   *311*

LETTER: To L.S. Senghor   *313*

Renewal Time

Though action rages without, the heart can be tuned to produce unbroken music.

So said Acharya Vinoba Bhave, replaying the Hindu scriptures from the Bhagavad-Gita for his fellow prisoners, out there in India in 1932. This, my people, is my unbroken music. Come around, let's talk. When music travels in the wind, who can stop your ears except yourself? Come on over, let us talk. In years to come, when this will be an undivided house and we'll be done spilling blood and guts, and justice and peace and plenty will be what a decent house should contain, we shall most of us remember the history of these times. Remember maybe also the voices we hear from the whirlwind, the dirges that we make; the songs we hear from far away lands where our players refuse to hang up their harps, because they daren't forget this lovely bleeding land, lest their tongues cleave to the roof of the mouth, lest the ancestors torment them. If these our songs are not remembered in the years to come, amid prosperity or amid other stresses that demand another language, no matter.

Our social concerns change or shift from time to time; the music of today may not raise any applause tomorrow. The memory of singular bleakness or brightness or brownness of past winters or summers or autumns may teach us nothing in particular for this year. But the seasons link up in our own or inherited consciousness, through the years, decades, centuries. The seasons are the unbroken music of our communal experience.

'If you must measure time into seasons, let each season encircle all the other seasons, and let today embrace the past with remembrance, the future with longing.' So said Kahlil ·Gibran. We can remember, whether *we* lived through the seasons or not, the rituals of initiation, of planting, of harvesting — the unbroken celebration of life and death, of triumph or defeat, of heroism and love. They merge with or become seasons of the mind and heart. Here they are immortalised.

And so mine is only one kind of music in the orchestration of our time, which latter is only one segment of time in the cumulative, continuing poetry of our people.

We dreamed once of a house undivided: we began consciously to dream of it when our African pioneers formed a national movement in 1912. And I use 'dreamed' not to refer to a 'fancy' or a toying with an idea. Those pioneers were an enlightened leadership, and could use only the conventional methods of pleading. We all know the excruciating penalty their successors paid in the sixties for daring to push further the ideal of an undivided house, an ideal born of an ancient humanism. And now we sing on two sides of a wall, simulating a formidable deafness. We peep through chinks and swinging doors and glass windows to see each other across the barriers. And in broad daylight those who tower over us and their own gods themselves put on dark goggles and say what they see is not real. Flashes, silhouettes, profiles are all we are prepared to see. Why, why?

After we were hurt, after our humanism met with an uncompromisingly cruel rebuff, we thought we could withdraw, take cover in our own blackness. This time consciously. Unlike hitherto when we took our blackness for granted. Because we had never been made to forget we are black. 'Never to forget' had to give way to 'always remember'. And then when the people began 'always to remember' they had to pay the penalty all over again. Because it was interpreted as 'always remember the other man is white'. Why, why?

We keep on talking across the wall, singing our different songs, beating our different drums. And yet the artist, always the spearpoint of a people's sensitivity, cannot but feel and express the paradoxes, the ironies, the stupidities, the follies, the resilience, the fortitude, the fears, the ignorance, the tenderness, the hypocrisies, the yearnings, all these deep-deep down, seeping through between our ghettoes white and black, deep down under the foundation of this wall. He can penetrate the social scene in which a people kick about and yell in the attempt to bust the links and disengage from history, because they are entangled with those they deem inferior. The artist pauses, wonders how it must be for anyone to invest all his money, all his time and strength, all his life, in the struggle to live outside of history. If the artist tries to ignore all these realities, it could be because he/she is a prisoner of tribal taboos and other superstitions. Or else he/she is not all there. And we know that in our case, the system was forced upon us. We paid too dearly for our humanism, oh so dearly. Are we going to be made to pay for consolidating our humanism for our separate areas? Once more? May the ancestors cover our naked bodies!

The seepage under the foundation of the wall is but the southern expression of the entangled destinies of black and white. Since the Portuguese touched the coast of Africa, west and later east, the histories of Europe and Africa have been intertwined, flowing into each other. Wherever walls were erected by the race-conscious Europeans, the water could only sink into the ground in order to flow. Because something's *got* to flow, *something* has got to flow, wherever two persons find each other face to face day after day. You might lay concrete on your side of the wall. Unless you have the means and skill to pave all the fragmented land on his side of the wall, the water from his side must take to subterranean channels and undermine your foundation.

And so we find ourselves in part expressing African thoughts, an African sensibility, in Bantu languages, in English and a few of us in Afrikaans. Fashionable phrases like 'protest literature', 'addressing white people', 'addressing blacks' can be too simplistic. Especially as our literary media are separate. Right there the readership is split down the middle. Africans are exposed to English literature by whites as well as to their own, whites are excluded from African literature.

Which way now, which way? Any wonder that whites feature less and less in African writing at home? Unimportant? No. Maybe simply irrelevant to the black man's understanding of himself, another rejection of the seepage, the flow, down there, underground. A reaction to rejection. But the unbroken music will go on. Though the world outside rages, though the winds whip and lash around, the heart can be tuned.

Come on over . . . let us talk.

Some years to come, when the house will no longer be divided, we may chat about these times of pain.

And the season of creations will encircle the season of harvesting which will embrace the season of death which will encircle the season of waiting and enduring, spinning out the unbroken song of a people.

The poem, the tale, the play, the direct prose statement of social man all make up the unbroken song. *None of its notes is final,* says Tagore, *yet each reflects the infinite.* By infinite I understand the continuity of the imagination, its perpetual renewal. Toni Cade Bambara, the Afro-American fiction writer, tells us that literature should make revolution irresistible. By revolution I understand renewal. We must come to this song of powerful, memorable, beautiful words for renewal. To help us get our minds and our hearts together. That's how it goes for the rest of the world. In each community the renewal has a cultural purpose, its own.

Introduction to the Stories

He came out of Amanzimtoti in 1940 with a twenty-one-year-old head full of itself, stuck on itself. At 21 you feel you're the centre of the universe. You want to take on the world. And yet you're a mere parcel of confusion. There's a mighty heave in your biology. As if to prepare you for the pole-vault event of your life. And you feel the strain and pain of that heave. Because you're black your aspirations, your hopes, have little to do with social realities. The rapid fluctuations between the high and the low make for dizzy spells, so to speak. The high because you strive to shoot for regions clear of the muck and smell and all the getting-through objectives set for you as a boy. The low because you're hemmed in, because someone fenced you in and then turned round and told you, 'It's rough out there among us white folks; could break you if you tried to compete with us; be warned and enjoy your freedom from unequal competition.'

Too scared to move into teaching just yet, he ventured into an unexpected world, the world of the blind and the deaf-mutes. Ezenzeleni, Itereleng,

Kutlwanong, Roodepoort, Hammanskraal. Secretarial work, social work, a little teaching, driving, the lot. He waded into this world armed only with a feeble lantern — a pre-matric teacher's certificate.

He responded to the mighty heave, to the urge to write verse and then stories. Stories came pouring out of his head. And he wrote. Fun, exhilaration, escape. He responded to the call to say what was in his soul. The desire to create strong beautiful words. For what publisher? None. *The Bantu World? Ilanga lase Natal?* Hardly. They wanted only short-short sketches, less verse. *Drum* was still to be born, almost a decade later. But the heat was on. He wrote for its own sake. For some inner freedom and peace, for equilibrium in a ship riding the formidable spill of the high seas right in the eye of a storm.

And so 1946, *Man Must Live.* A small volume brought out as an experiment by the publisher, Julian Rollnick of African Bookman, Cape Town.

More stories later. Joined the black voices of the fifties coming through *Drum*. Some appeared in *Drum*, others elsewhere. 'The Master of Doornvlei', 'Dinner at Eight', 'Down the Quiet Street', 'The Coffee-cart Girl', 'The Woman', 'The Woman Walks Out', 'The Suitcase'.

Exile. First stop Lagos, Nigeria. For a long time the South African scene dominates the mind. Holds on tenaciously for fear of being forgotten. 'The Living and the Dead', 'He and the Cat'.

Next stop Paris, France. The fifth year. Two years in France: the first you spend learning the language and ways of the French. You resist involvement. Gay Paris? You wonder. Its night life, maybe. Its boulevards, pleasant to walk on. But you want people. You can't talk with night life, with boulevards, with the arts of another culture. Talking in the sense of communing. You even become sensitive to some crudities and streak of cruelty in the French others might not observe. You try to accommodate, or be accommodated by, a city so many people say is wonderful. Some people may enjoy the wine only and stick to that. And you? You're eclectic, and that helps. But you don't want to be involved and thus *forget* where you came from. Yet you want people. So you keep busy at work and write in your free time. To insulate yourself.

The Nigerian memory is still fresh. Hence 'The Barber of Bariga' and 'A Ballad of Oyo'. The deep South continues to claim you. Hence 'A Point of Identity', 'Grieg on a Stolen Piano', 'In Corner B' and 'Mrs Plum'.

Blind Alley

What have I to do with thee?
A house of sack is waiting yonder,
Moroka there is full and calling.
Come, my love,
We'll seek our own.
Moroka's waiting, calling, yonder.
We'll make our paradise, we two,
Moroka's sacks are calling.
We'll lose ourselves among the crowds.
Moroka's beckoning, calling, waiting;
And what have I to do with thee?

So the tragic song of Moroka goes. Squalid sack shanties calling. Squalid, narrow streets repelling and calling. Some lose themselves here. Others don't. Some lose their hates, loves; others stick out their jaw and live above the flat shanties, the dirty streets swarming with flies. Many revolt against these things, against their wives; their husbands, their parents. But Moroka continues to sprawl up the hill, made by the people in it, making the people in it.

Ditsi Makwe came to put up his shanty soon after
Moroka began. His friend, John Seeku, had lent him
money when Ditsi came to Johannesburg from
Bochem. Their fathers were friends and once room-
mates for several years at the Denver hostel.

'Take care of my son in that jungle city,' Ditsi's
father had written to the older Seeku when Ditsi
came to the city for the first time.

'I'm sure when the two boys get to know each
other they will help each other along.'

They got to know each other. They became
friends: John, man of the world, of impulsive
decisions, and not so serious; Ditsi, just another man,
with violent convictions, when he had any. But the
older Seeku was not to know his friend's son long.
For within a fortnight of Ditsi's arrival, the old man
died.

'I don't know how I shall ever repay you,' said
Ditsi to his new companion.

John had kept quiet. Many a time he felt secretly
that he had done this for Ditsi's wife, whom he found
an admirable person; more than he would like to
admit. Ditsi had brought his wife and two children
with him. A pretty woman of about 30, with big,
dark eyes, thick lips, and of medium build. She took
a factory job as a machinist, and Ditsi worked in a
department store. He was happy with Thamila, his
wife, and their children.

John Seeku, not married himself, visited the
Makwe's shelter often. He was treated as one of the
family, being amiable and not wanting to remind
them of their debt.

'Our struggle is a hard one. But we must not let our
people down. You see here tin and sack shanties. You

and I have to continue to live in them. Your children
and mine have to continue to cough in these leaky
shanties. Winter is coming on. We cannot wait any
longer. We must fight for decent houses . . . '

And so the man spoke on. He was speaking to a
handful of men on an open place. They could not
have numbered more than ten.

This Sunday morning Ditsi Makwe was passing on
his way to John's. He stopped an old bearded man
just crossing the street to join the audience.

'What meeting is this?' he inquired of the grey
head.

'Do you not know of the meeting?'

'I should not ask, old father.'

'Are you not of these parts?'

'Yes, I am, old father.'

'How long are you here?'

'A month.'

'Then you must be asleep, young man.'

'What meeting is it, old father?'

The old man looked up into Ditsi's face with soft
glistening eyes.

'That is Fube,' the crackling voice said, evasively.

'Who is Fube?'

'You do not know him? A brave young man. Says
his mind and the devil-take-the-hindmost. Looks a
man straight in the face, and does not blink. That's
the man for me.'

'But what are they here for?' Ditsi felt impatient.

'You do not know? You have not seen anything
yet, young man.'

Ditsi sighed.

'We want houses,' as if to reply to the sigh, 'that's
what we are here for.' And the old man made to cross
the street, to demonstrate that he was one of 'we'.

Ditsi shook his head and proceeded on his way. Fube's voice rang out in the same strain.

Ditsi gradually began to understand things. He got to know Moroka — her bitterness, her pains, her frustration, and her lust for life. This understanding brought him in close association with Fube and all the others who felt and thought as he did. He attended all Fube's meetings, because Fube's cause, Moroka's cause, was his, and he gave to it all he was capable of. Ditsi often felt like a man who is carried on the crest of a wave, so necessary, if not altogether inevitable.

Thamila was just putting the children to bed when she heard a hard knock at the door. Her heart missed a beat or two.

'Who's there?'

'Nkomo.'

'Who's Nkomo?'

'You do not know me, then?'

'No.'

'Open. Then you will see and know me.'

'I cannot if I do not know you.'

'I must come in. I bring you news about your husband.'

'Who's my husband?'

A sinister chuckle from outside. 'Oh, I see. Your man is Makwe.'

Thamila's imagination ran wild, even in those few seconds before she opened the door.

A big man with broad shoulders and a big stomach entered, a big club in his hand. He was panting fast from a weak heart. His eyes were red fire and looked savage. He sat down.

'You are Mother Makwe?' He did not wait for an answer. 'Your husband is in great danger. He is playing with fire, taunting the lion in its den. Sit down, good woman.' Thamila sat on the edge of a chair, trying to avoid the focus of those terrible, bulging balls of fire.

'I've only come to ask you, as a good woman who doesn't want any dust, to advise Makwe. He is one of those rebels who fly above the heads of those the people chose as fathers of Moroka. I must answer for the actions of everybody here. I know what the people want. If he continues to attend these rebel meetings and mislead the people, the wolves will eat him. This house will be burnt down, and you may be disgraced anywhere in Moroka by men who know their work. The people do not pay their dues to me any more. They are being told we are cheats. Tell him to be careful. Tell him that, good woman, tell him that. Tell him.'

The poor woman had nothing to say. Nkomo was satisfied with the effect of his words. She was clearly alarmed.

Every time Thamila turned in her blankets that fearful night she seemed to see big red bulging balls of fire, a big stomach; in the dark, a woman crying, disgraced by men who know their work. She saw Ditsi lying there clawed by the deadly paws of a monster of no name, no shape, a monster that was Moroka. The haunting figure of a tall man. Then his husky, pitiless voice: Tell him that good woman . . . Tell him that . . . Tell him.

She uncovered her head and stared at the candle, which seemed to be burning into an eternal night . . .

'I think it is all rubbish.'

'What is?'

'All these meetings. Takes us nowhere. Get a good house, you still need many more things.' John Seeku was in an unusually serious mood.

'But you never really get a good house,' said Ditsi. 'Put a man in a filthy place like this, you've condemned his soul to filth.'

'I'm thinking of your safety, yours and Thamila's and the children's. After it all, who thanks you? This place is brutal. There is always something lurking in the shadows here, ready to strike and destroy.'

Thamila looked up at John. Ditsi looked at both of them. He wanted to tell them all that he thought and felt. He felt deeply. He could not tell them that he was caught in a stream. A stream of fire; that he felt he could not stand outside it, outside this scalding stream; that he was going to continue in his defiance of the elected upper dogs of Moroka who spat venom in the path of those like him.

He looked at his wife. He was horrified by what he saw on Thamila's face. The placid, smooth face was convulsed with some repelling feeling she could not conceal; something like a mixture of pain and bitter reproach.

Poor woman! Ditsi thought, looking away from her, you have lived a comparatively quiet life. Born at a mission station. No crises in your life until now. Perhaps no bitter tears. 'Frightened little woman,' he said aloud, going to embrace her. She stiffened, seeming to pull away. Ditsi released his hold.

Ditsi realised the break had come. The break he had always feared. He knew he could not take it. At times he almost burst into tears. He took the children away to his parents.

It was quite plain to Thamila's simple mind: she

had loved Ditsi with the warmest affection a man can hope for. She looked up to him as the main pillar of her security. Now that sense of security was shaky, if not lost . . .

Every night now there were group meetings. More and more people flocked to these meetings; their leaders spoke their language: it was a matter of shelter for flesh and blood.

Ditsi found Thamila gone one night when he came back from one of these meetings. Her clothing was not there.

Impulsively he dashed out of the house into the thick night. He did not know where he was going. Nor did he care. His one thought was to find Thamila.

He moved on and on into the night, a buzzing, brutal night, charged with the air of rebellion while Moroka screamed away in pain, sloth and sordidness. He must have been walking for more than four hours. He sat down, feeling only now his heavy limbs. Then he heard someone cough. Surely he was intimately familiar with that cough, he thought, starting. Or was it an illusion? He stood up.

By the gods, this is John's house! It was right in front of him. By degrees its peculiar shape registered in his mind in the dim light of an autumn dawn. He crossed over to reassure himself.

They were lying beside the wall. Two people gazing into each other's eyes.

Then one of them struck a match, evidently to light a cigarette. He saw her face. What fate brought him here to see what he now saw? By the gods! Could this be true? He gulped down a lump in the throat, and turned his back to them, a broken man . . .

The day came. Thousands of people marched

through the streets of Moroka. The settlement was one seething mass of blind hate, blind anger, frustration. Ditsi was there and yet not there. Nagging thoughts were milling inside him, about John, about Thamila. He thought of the ironic twist in his affairs: wanting a decent house with no home to house . . . Ignorant fool!

They were nearing the location office when one of the elected men was pounced upon.

Yells, sticks cracking in the air. A group of the victim's supporters dashing and throwing themselves upon the masses. Screams and yells. Mad riot. A police van swerving round the corner. Three policemen jumping out, charging with revolvers in hand. Madness at the sight of pistols. Ditsi rushing to the front ranks in mad, almost unconscious determination. His club falling on the skull of the policeman with an ominous crack. Another blow. Policeman in the dust. Ditsi's savage boot on the face. Death, white death looking at. him through glazed eyes. Mad stampeding. All in a few moments. Two policemen killed. Moroka gave a shattering cry which shot up, hung in the misty air and seemed to fall into groaning and wailing fragments.

He felt terrible joy after it all. And then he felt a little dizzy. He left the yelling crowd with a few other men. He had never drunk heavily. This day he was going to get drunk, by the spirits!

And he did. He boarded a bus. Again he didn't care where he was going. Just to get away. Away from — he didn't know nor care from what.

Within a few minutes Ditsi found himself on Nancefield station.

'Two policemen killed . . . .

'Two what?'

'Two policemen I say. Killed. On the spot.'

'By whom?'

'The people. You should have seen their mad fury . . . Black man doesn't want to see a revolver.'

'Shocking. Fearful. Hm. Man dies today, man hangs tomorrow. Simply like that . . . '

He heard all this faintly, as if the voices came from a deep dungeon. So hollow. Ridiculously hollow. He chuckled, really tickled.

He was standing on the platform, gazing at the railway line. A green electric engine was coming from the south side. It made a thin siren sound. Ridiculously thin and sharp. A big, green rumbling engine, producing a sound like that of a cycle hooter. And as it rumbled past Ditsi laughed aloud, really tickled. He went under the bridge to the other end.

They were there. John and Thamila. His wife. He came and stood close to them. They were clearly embarrassed.

'Oh, waking from your beautiful dreams, eh, you two?' He swayed unsteadily, drunk. Thamila was quiet.

'What do you mean, Ditsi? Tell me, how did the procession go?'

'You want to know, eh? You t-two clever b-birds — hic — caught in y-your n-nest, eh? Th-Thamila, my — wife — you l-love him, eh? Clever b-boy this — n-not s-s-slow and — hic — stup-stupid like m-me, eh?' He belched. Thamila was looking at him all the time.

'When is this bloody train coming? No matches. Should a man, yes, should a man help a woman, another man's woman, lose all trust and faith in her man? Should he? I mean should he or not?'

'No, no, no. I've n-nothing to do with you.' He

pointed at John. 'Now, you, Thamila. Look at me, look at John. Today, this day, now, tell us whom you want to have.' Thamila was clearly in a difficulty. She showed it. 'Come, come, come, Thamila. Now, just now, I mean, say it.'

Ditsi swayed one way and another.

Then she took a step forward, head bent, and looked straight into Ditsi's eyes. Almost throwing herself onto him, she laid her head on his chest and cried, bitterly. John's outer crust cracked and he felt wounded at the sight of the drama. The pain of wounded pride slowly became the pain of regret as he remembered Ditsi's words of a few moments before. He had summed up John's betrayal well; but he had put the choice to his wife.

As he left the station, however, he had mixed feelings about this episode of his life.

Ditsi lifted her head up, so that their eyes met. They understood. Thamila wanted to lead him to the steps of the bridge. But he stood still, exerting his willpower to keep himself steady.

'Are you coming back, Thamila?'

She nodded.

'Not just because — because I'm drunk and you want a soul to rescue?'

She shook her head. 'It has not been easy for me all these weeks, Ditsi.' Then she burst into sobs. They understood.

He felt awkward. And he made no effort to comfort her. He only knew that she was in his arms now. 'I shall never forget this in all my life,' she said. There was profound peace inside him.

'There he is! This is the man!' Ditsi turned round, to see a black man with huge shoulders and a big stomach point an ominous finger at him, leading a white constable towards him.

Thamila saw him and recognised him, the big man. Fear gripped her again.

Ditsi's mind was becoming clearer. He remembered it all. Policeman killed, hanging or a life sentence. The ghastliness of it all. He surrendered, looking at Thamila for the last time as a man free to move among his people. She understood. And it hurt too much to allow any tears.

The Suitcase

One of these days he was going to take a desperate chance, Timi thought. He would not miss it if it presented itself. Many men had got rich by sheer naked chance. Couldn't it just be that he was destined to meet such a chance?

He sat on a pavement on a hot afternoon. It was New Year's Eve. And in such oppressive heat Timi had been sitting for over an hour. An insect got into his nostril and made him sneeze several times. Through the tears that filled his eyes the traffic seemed to dance about before him.

The grim reality of his situation returned to him with all its cold and aching pain after the short interlude with the insect. Today he had been led on something like a goosechase. He had been to three places where the chance of getting work was promising. He had failed. At one firm he had been told, 'We've already got a boy, Jim.' At the second firm a tiny typist told him, 'You're too big, John. The boss wants a small boy — about eighteen you know.' Then she had gone on with her typing, clouding her white face with cigarette smoke. At the third place of call a short pudgy white man put down his price in a squeaking voice: 'Two pounds ten a week.' Three pounds ten a week, Timi had said. 'Take it or leave it, my boy,' the proprietor had said as his final word, and snorted to close the matter. Timi chuckled softly to himself at the thought of the pudgy man with fat white cheeks and small blinking eyes.

He was watching the movements of a wasp tormenting a worm. The wasp circled over the worm and then came down on the clumsy and apparently defenceless worm. It seemed to stand on its head as it stung the worm. The worm wriggled violently, seeming to want to fly away from the earth. Then suddenly the worm stretched out, as though paralysed. The winged insect had got its prey. Timi felt pity for the poor worm. An unequal fight, an unfair fight, he thought. Must it always be thus, he asked — the well-armed and agile creatures sting the defenceless to death? The wasp was now dragging the worm; to its home, evidently.

He remembered he had nothing to take home. But the thought comforted him that his wife was so understanding. A patient and understanding wife. Yes, she would say, as she had often said, 'Tomorrow's sun must rise, Timi. It rises for every-one. It may have its fortunes.' Or, 'I will make a little fire, Timi. Our sages say even where there is no pot to boil there should be a fire.'

Now she was ill. She was about to have a baby; a third baby. And with nothing to take home for the last two months, his savings running out, he felt something must be done. Not anything that would get him into jail. No, not that. It wouldn't do for him to go to jail with his wife and children almost starving like that. No, he told himself emphatically.

A white man staggered past him, evidently drunk. He stopped a short way past Timi and turned to look at him. He walked back to Timi and held out a bottle of brandy before him, scarcely keeping firm on his legs.

'Here, John, drink this stuff. Happy New Year!' Timi shook his head.

'C'mon, be — be a s-sport, hic! No p-police to catch you, s-s-see?'

Timi shook his head again and waved him away.

'Huh, here's a bugger don't want to have a happy New Year, eh. Go t-to hell then.'

The white man swung round, brandishing his bottle as he tripped away.

If only that were money, Timi thought bitterly.

He remembered it was time to go home, and boarded a bus to Sophiatown. In the bus he found an atmosphere of revelry. The New Year spirit, he thought; an air of reckless abandon. Happy New Year! one shouted at intervals.

Timi was looking at a man playing a guitar just opposite him, across the aisle. A girl was dancing to the rhythm of the music. The guitarist strummed on, clearly carried away in the flight of his own music. He coaxed, caressed and stroked his instrument. His long fingers played effortlessly over the strings. He glowered at the girl in front of him with a hanging lower lip as she twisted her body seductively this way and that, like a young supple plant that the wind plays about with. Her breasts pushed out under a light sleeveless blouse. At the same time the guitarist bent his ear to the instrument as if to hear better its magic notes, or to whisper to it the secret of his joy.

Two young women came to sit next to Timi. One of them was pale, and seemed sick. The other deposited a suitcase between her leg and Timi's. His attention was taken from the music by the presence of these two women. They seemed to have much unspoken between them.

At the next stop they rose to alight. Timi's one eye was fixed on the suitcase as he watched them go towards the door. When the bus moved a man who was sitting behind Timi exclaimed, 'Those young women have left their case.'

'No, it is mine,' said Timi hastily.

'No. I saw them come in with it.'

This is a chance . . .

'I tell you it's mine.'

'You can't tell me that.'

Now there mustn't be any argument, or else . . .

'Did you not see me come in with a case?'

I mustn't lose my temper, or else . . .

'Tell the truth, my man, it bites no one.'

'What more do you want me to say?'

The people are looking at me now. By the gods, what can I do?

'It's his lucky day,' shouted someone from the back, 'let him be!'

'And if it is not his, how is this a lucky day?' asked someone else.

'Ha, ha, ha!' A woman laughed. 'You take my thing, I take yours, he takes somebody else's. So we all have a lucky day, eh? Ha, ha, ha.' She rocked with voluble laughter, seeming to surrender herself to it.

'Oh, leave him alone,' an old voice came from another quarter, 'only one man saw the girls come in with a suitcase, and only one man says it is his. One against one. Let him keep what he has, the case. Let the other man keep what he has, the belief that it belongs to the girls.' There was a roar of laughter. The argument melted in the air of a happy New Year, of revelry and song.

Timi felt a great relief. He had won.

The bus came to a stop and he alighted. He did not even hear someone behind him in the bus cry, 'That suitcase will yet tell whom it belongs to, God is my witness!' Why can't people mind their own affairs? He thought of all those people looking at him.

Once out of the bus he was seized by a fit of curiosity, anxiety and expectancy. He must get home quickly and see what is in the case.

It was a chance, a desperate chance, and he had taken it. That mattered to him most as he paced up the street.

Timi did not see he was about to walk into a crowd of people. They were being searched by the police, two white constables. He was jolted into attention by the shining of a badge. Quickly he slipped into an open backyard belonging to a Chinese. Providence was with him, he thought, as he ran to stand behind the great iron door, his heart almost choking him.

He must have waited there for fifteen minutes, during which he could see all that was happening out there in the street. The hum and buzz so common to Good Street rose to a crescendo; so savage, so cold-blooded, so menacing. Suddenly he got a strange and frightening feeling that he had excited all this noise, that he was the centre around which these angry noises whirled and circled, that he had raised a hue and cry.

For one desperate second he felt tempted to leave the case where he squatted. It would be so simple for him, he thought. Yes, just leave the case there and

have his hands, no, more than that, his soul, freed of
the burden. After all, it was not his.

Not his. This thought reminded him that he had
done all this because it was not his. The incident in
the bus was occasioned by the stark naked fact that
the case was not his. He felt he must get home soon
because it was not his. He was squatting here like an
outlaw, because the case was not his. Why not leave it
here then, after all these efforts to possess it and keep
it? There must surely be valuable articles in it, Timi
mused. It was so heavy. There must be. It couldn't be
otherwise. Else why had Providence been so kind to
him so far? Surely the spirits of his ancestors had pity
on him; with a sick wife and hungry children. Then
the wild, primitive determination rose in him; the
blind determination to go through with a task once
begun, whether a disaster can be avoided in time or
not, whether it is to preserve worthless or valuable
articles. No, he was not going to part with the case.

The pick-up van came and collected the detained
men and women. The police car started up the street.
Timi came out and walked on the pavement, not
daring to look behind, lest he lose his nerve and
blunder. He knew he was not made for all this sort of
thing. Pitso was coming up the pavement in the
opposite direction. Lord, why should it be Pitso at
this time? Pitso, the gas-bag, the notorious talker
whose appearance always broke up a party. They
met.

'Greetings! You seem to be in a hurry, Timi?' Pitso
called out in his usual noisy and jovial fashion. 'Are
you arriving or going?'

'Arriving.' Timi did not want to encourage him.

'Ha, since when have you been calling yourself
A.J.B.?'

'Who says I'm A.J.B.?'

'There, my friend.' Pitso pointed at the large initials on the case, and looked at his friend with laughing eyes.

'Oh, it's my cousin's.' Timi wished he could wipe the broad stupid grin off the mouth of this nonentity. He remembered later how impotent and helpless he had felt. For Pitso and his grin were inseparable, like Pitso and his mouth. Just now he wished he wouldn't look so uneasy. 'I'm sorry, Pitso, my wife isn't well, and I must hurry.' He passed on. Pitso looked at his friend, his broad mouth still smiling blankly.

The Chevrolet came to a stop just alongside the pavement. Then it moved on, coasting idly and carelessly.

'Hey!' Timi looked to his left. Something seemed to snap inside him and release a lump shooting up to his throat. 'Stop, *jong!*' The driver waved to him.

There they were, two white constables and an African in plain clothes in the back seat. Immediately he realised it would be foolish to run. Besides, the case should be his. He stopped. The driver went up to him and wrenched the suitcase from Timi's hand. At the same time he caught him by the shoulder and led him to the car, opening the back door for Timi. The car shot away to the police-station.

His knees felt weak when he recognised the black man next to him. It was the man who had sat behind him on the bus and argued that the case was not Timi's. By the spirits, did the man have such a strong sense of justice as to call God to be witness? Even on New Year's Eve? Or was he a detective? No, he could have arrested him on the bus. The man hardly looked at Timi. He just looked in front of him in a self-righteous posture, as it struck Timi.

Timi got annoyed; frantically annoyed. It was a challenge. He would face it. Things might turn round somewhere. He felt he needed all the luck fate could afford to give him.

At the police-station the two constables took the case into a small room. After a few minutes they came out, with what Timi thought was a strange communication of feelings between them as they looked at each other.

'*Kom, kom, jong!*' one of them said, although quite gently. They put the case in front of him.

'Whose case is this?'

'Mine.'

'Do you have your things in here?'

'My wife's things.'

'What are they?'

'I think she has some of her dresses in it.'

'Why do you say you *think?*'

'Well, you see, she just packed them up in a hurry, and asked me to take them to her aunt; but I didn't see her pack them.'

'Hm. You can recognise your wife's clothing?'

'Some of it.' Why make it so easy for him? And why was there such cold amusement in the white man's eyes?

The constable opened the suitcase, and started to unpack the articles one by one.

'Is this your wife's?' It was a torn garment.

'Yes.'

'And this? And this?' Timi answered yes to both. Why did they pack such torn clothing? The constable lifted each one up before Timi. Timi's thoughts were racing and milling round in his head. What trick was fate about to play him? He sensed there was something wrong. Had he been a dupe?

The constable, after taking all the rags out, pointed to an object inside. *'And is this also your wife's?'* He glared at Timi with aggressive eyes.

Timi stretched his neck to see.

It was a ghastly sight: A dead baby that could not have been born more than twelve hours before. A naked, white, curly-haired image of death. Timi gasped and felt sick and faint. They had to support him to the counter to make a statement. He told the truth. He knew he had gambled with chance; the chance that was to cost him eighteen months' hard labour.

The Woman

'She is there!' When Africans say a person 'is there', they mean you cannot but feel she is alive: she allows you no room to forget she was born and is alive in flesh and spirit.

'A mother-in-law has great duties to perform and great principles to live for,' the woman used to say. Because she was so aware of these duties and principles, 'Madira (for this is the woman we are talking about) always behaved and spoke as if she were the only person God deemed fit to fashion after the pattern of the true mother-in-law. On a morning, usually a Sunday morning, when she knew that men as well as women were home, 'Madira would take up her shawl, walk out with a great sweep of the arm, and take long, lounging strides from one house to another, propounding her theory before man and wife.

'Madira was a meddlesome woman. At the time we take up her story, she was nearer sixty than fifty. She was a thin, spectre-like figure. Her chest curved in a little. Her whole physical make-up seemed to consist of taut strings which would one day snap and bring chaos and hell-fire upon the whole township.

When she looked at you, her eyes seemed to wander over the area of your body first, and then to focus on your eyes. One of her greatest boasts was that she always looked at a person in the face after sizing him up. In view of the fact that traditionally African women dare not look men in the face, let alone size them up, many women of her age regarded this as a special quality of boldness in 'Madira.

The name ''Madira' fitted her well, or she fitted the name well. 'Dira' means enemies.

'A good wife must be obedient to her mother-in-law; she must be able to wash, clean, cook, tend the house and look after her children well,' she always said. 'But the young girls we have today for daughters-in-law, pooh! They are thick-headed, lazy and stubborn.'

If anyone among her listeners did not agree, she told the others after 'Madira had left — 'Ha, you cannot teach that woman anything!' Then they would nod their heads in agreement.

'Whatever did your son see in this girl when he married her?' 'Madira asked of a woman one day in the latter's house. The woman had come to visit her son. 'Madira had merely come because she wanted to know this respectable young man's mother.

'What do you mean?' asked the woman.

'I mean she is so lazy. A young woman should go out and work to help her husband earn money. She cannot even cook!'

Her listener was much too abashed to say anything in reply.

'She reminds me of a young woman I used to know some years ago. The woman used to sit in front of her

house on a winter morning and bask in the sun. I tell
you, good woman, she would sit there before cleaning
the house or washing her baby or even her own face.
The child would climb up to the breast without any
help from the mother. A fly would walk on her face,
starting its journey from under the mouth right up to
the forehead, without so much as an effort on her
part to wave it away. Only in the late afternoon when
the husband would be coming home did the lazy
creature stand up to do something. Rumour had it
those days that the husband was also a dull-brained
fool because, it was said, he had drunk tea into
which, out of sheer laziness to go and buy milk
around the corner, she had squeezed out her own
milk. I should not be surprised if the story is true!'

Then 'Madira would say, 'You young mothers
should take your children out more often. In my day
I used to take Joel to the tennis-court. There he
waited in a small cart while I played tennis — this way
and that.' Here 'Madira often tickled her listeners by
waving her hands left and right alternately, as a two-
handed player might do. Both those who had grown
up with her, and those who were comparative
strangers to her, shook their heads vigorously and
incredulously.

When she talked tennis, 'Madira often spoke
English — as much as she could remember — to the
total dislike and contempt of many older folk. Nor
did she ever forget to mention that she had once been
a schoolmistress, trained at the Wilberforce Institute.
'When I was a schoolmistress . . . ' she often began —
which was enough to make the other women feel at
once jealous, envious, annoyed, and humble. If
'Madira did anything good, it was because she had
been a schoolmistress; if she did anything she was

lucky to be able to acknowledge as bad, she was thankful that she had done nothing worse, because she had been a schoolmistress.

'Madira had been married twice. The first husband lived with her three years and then 'the bell rang for stopping work', as Africans say when relations are severed, and he disappeared. Some say he could not fit into her hard school. Others say she could not impose the government over him she would have liked to. The two explanations amounted to the same thing. She herself said: 'You see, be good to a man, do everything for him, give him good food, mend his clothes, tell him how to keep clean and keep him clean, give him all the comfort, and he leaves you!'

The second husband stayed two years with her. Two years of nagging, spying, of scandal. He was very sorry for having given her a daughter. He would rather have left nothing on earth that would constantly remind him of her.

The first impulse when her second husband left was for the woman to visit her neighbours and virtually hold a spear before them to listen to her woes. 'Now I know,' 'Madira said with genuine bitterness, 'who are answerable for this suffering I am going through.' They looked at her, tacitly demanding an explanation, for 'Madira was the last person they ever expected to suffer, still less did they expect her to admit it. 'I know the women who go about defiling my name by telling all kinds of lies about me. But I shall not mention their names. You know I do not want to speak ill of people and say so-and-so has done this and that. Yes, some of us sit on our troubles so that no one notices them. But one day the wind will sound their names in your ears. I know my husbands could only have been dragged away by some women. The people of this township hate me. They are jealous because I am cleaner than any of them at any time of any day. Have you ever seen any of my husbands go about in torn or dirty clothes?'

Her listeners looked at one another, nodded their heads, looked back at her, gave a click with the tongue, gave a clap of the hands, dovetailed their hands in front of them, and shook their heads with affected or genuine indignation for 'Madira's sake.

The third man in her life did not marry her by common law. 'They simply lived together,' we say, as if marriage by civil law were like scaling a slippery wall. A son, Joel by name, was born of this union, which lasted ten years.

Trouble came when the woman one day said to her man, 'Old Man, you have the money and I have the brain.' Her man raised his eyebrows and prepared himself. 'We can go and buy an old tram-body — you know those the City Council threw away near Croesus Station — then we can paint it well, and put a coffee-house hereabouts.'

After her man had thought it over, his only reply was that he had no money, at any rate for such mad schemes.

'Madira was not to be waved aside. She repeated the matter several times, until her man left her one day, never to be seen in our township again.

'Men are stupid, you know,' she said, 'the ancestors help me that I should have seen anything wonderful in their thick heads!' Other men said, 'That the man should have been reared by that woman for ten years! And to think that when he came under her armpit, we spat on our hands and pointed into the heavens, swearing that if he stayed five years with her, a cow would give birth to a mule!'

It was then that, having thus failed to run husbands, 'Madira decided to use all her genius (which she believed she had) in being a mother-in-law.

Her daughter was now full twenty-two. Like her younger half-brother, she could not go any higher at school than Standard VIII which they both failed to pass. This was always regretted by their mother.

'I have *two* children at the high school,' 'Madira used to tell her neighbours, indicating it with two long fingers. 'Some foolish people think it is easy to get children through high school. You have to work, work, work, and stint yourself rice and stew, and wear rough German print. I do not know what I shall do when they go to Fort Hare!' The woman sighed, gave a despairing clap of the hands and let her arms hang limp.

'The day those children go to Fort Hare,' said one old man, 'the spirits help me never to meet that woman!'

Dinko, the daughter, and Joel, the son, grew up under their mother's strict discipline. But while Joel was humble and subservient, Dinko was regarded as a rebellious little upstart who always had an answer ready on her precocious tongue.

'Madira was getting older and she wanted to see her dear children happily settled in married life. When a suitor came to see Dinko her mother kept a vigilant eye on the young man as though she wished she could shape him into the ideal son-in-law. Many were the nights when the young man came under the gaze of 'Madira. This unsettled him and he complained to Dinko, rather bashfully.

'Oh, it will not be long before we leave this house for good,' coaxed Dinko, bidding him be patient.

Dinko's young man, as 'Madira always referred to him, was a suitor long enough to study the prospective mother-in-law's ways and tastes.

She often said to her daughter: 'Your young man is too quiet for my liking. Such men can hardly be trusted. He will sit there as quiet as a mountain and say very little.'

To him she often said: 'I could never sit quiet like you, you know. When I was your age, I used to keep people listening attentively for hours.'

The two young people married. They left for their own two-roomed quarters at the east end of the township. 'Madira asked them many times to live with her, but they were both adamant in their decision. Dinko's husband had expressly told his wife that he could not think of being reared by his mother-in-law.

'You must remember, Mamma, that I belong to someone else now; it is not like being married to one's own brother — oh, what things am I saying now! But I am simply trying to make you under-stand, Mamma, that your own son would sooner live with you than another woman's son, such as my husband is.'

'You hurt me when you say that, Dinko. Yes, but you must remember, child, that I have lived long on this earth.' Then she enumerated a countless number of do's and don'ts to both, ending up with, 'Do not forget that the first baby must be born here. We must respect our custom.'

This was futile because Dinko's husband firmly made it clear to 'Madira that he was going to manage his affairs without her interference. From this day the woman always reminded Dinko, whenever they met, that her husband had no respect for old age and had talked to her as no young man, or even old man, had ever done.

'Just like the father, this girl Dinko,' she repeated to herself every time she thought of the 'lost couple'. The young couple's life was a happy one, notwithstanding the wrath of the ancestors which 'Madira predicted for them.

Joel was most devoted to his mother. 'Madira wanted some hold on somebody; she had it. Joel willingly became the tamed animal. He regarded it as a sacred duty to obey his mother implicitly. When her temper flared up, Joel was quick to ask her what had upset her, and coax her into a good temper. He married the woman of her choice — her old friend's daughter.

'No, child, that stove is not clean . . . '; 'No, child, you must not sit like that when you are in a family way . . . '; 'No, child, one does not cook cabbage in so much water . . . '; 'Your wash-towels need washing . . . '; 'Joel likes his egg boiled, not fried . . . '; 'Joel does not drink tea, he drinks water with plenty of milk in, and both the water and the milk must be hot . . . '

And so the orders were given. 'Madira was scrupulously clean. She worshipped cleanliness. It was a religion. Almost a neurosis. Every one of the three rooms and the step were not to be left dirty too long in the morning. She often had meat taken out of boiling water to be re-washed. She kept an eagle's eye over all the household duties. Anna obeyed without question, with the consoling feeling that she was doing it for Joel's sake. Her husband in turn was glad of it and told his vain self that his mother was fashioning a dutiful wife for him.

After the first year Anna showed signs of breaking.

She was becoming resentful of her mother-in-law's interfering with the management of their money and private affairs. She told Joel what she felt.

'You must not quarrel with Mother, Anna,' he replied with infuriating airs, 'I am sure she is doing it for the best of us all.'

'That's just the trouble,' Anna thought to herself, 'they are both such stupid persons that they do the worst and are convinced they are doing the best.' She felt miserably lonely.

When their first child was born, it was after many harrowing and embarrassing lectures on how to conduct herself while still pregnant. 'Madira believed in medical roots and herbs in spite of her education. And because she hated witches who walk 'naked at night', she warned her daughter-in-law against those friends with mischief behind their smiles. 'No sooner does a new life shoot out than some friend wants to kill it. Do not think that all people like to see you expecting a child. You will never know who has done you harm.'

Anna was perhaps too modern for 'Madira. But above all, she hated the mother-in-law's thrusting things upon her. The young woman looked to Joel for help; Joel merely looked at her with that blank and passive expression on his face. On such occasions she felt a growing hatred for her husband and for the woman from whose womb such a mass of confident and trusting stupidity had issued . . .

With the same apparent conviction that she was doing the best, 'Madira began to talk to the neighbours about her daughter-in-law's negligence, loss of respect and many other lapses. When Anna heard this she told Joel, only that he should be aware of it. Her inner self was revolted. She was feeling that she had borne too much.

The first quarrel began between Anna and Joel's mother. It was a bitter exchange of words. When Joel was informed, he warned his wife strongly.

Another bitter quarrel followed. Anna slapped her mother-in-law on the cheek. She looked at her hand as if she did not believe she could have been brought to this. She left 'Madira standing.

Everybody in the neighbourhood was shocked. Tongues were loosened. Some nodded their heads and said, 'It is good for 'Madira. She talks a little too much . . . ' 'We all talk,' said others, who held 'Madira's views about a mother-in-law's discipline, 'everybody talks. We are living in evil days when children beat their own mothers. Oh, spirits of our ancestors!'

They sighed, shook their heads, and looked at each other prophetically, as if to say, 'Yes, between you and me, I see the end of the world is near.' 'You just wait,' put in others who have the habit of predicting the future, 'just you wait! The day will come when the truth will show itself. God works in a mysterious way . . . '

Anna slapped her mother-in-law again one day. When Joel came back from work, he was beside himself with rage on hearing the report from a gossip who had been waiting at his gate to be the first to tell him. The informer ended by saying, 'You have married a hundred fires put together, Joel. That is the way with girls bred in town!'

'I think you will have to go, Anna, if you cannot treat my mother with respect. You do not seem to realize my mother is your mother!'

'It is right that I go, since you will always shut your eyes to the truth of the matter. I will take the child, and you will decide what to do. I have done all a human being can do in this kind of life. In truth, you find my mind already made up to leave. One thing I should like to say, Joel, is that you will never be able to keep a wife because your wife must also be your mother's wife. If your mother could help it, she would bear your own children for you.'

'Stop saying such things about my mother. It is enough that you have already lifted up your arm to beat her. I never knew I was marrying a monster. Oh, these town-bred women!'

'You're wrong there, I was born and bred in the country. As always, Joel, you will blame yourself, in spite of the fact that your mother did more than you to get me.'

Anna packed her belongings and sent them on to her home at Newclare. A divorce was granted in her favour.

Joel had been looking about for a wife with the help of his hard-working and loving mother. They came upon one — a pretty girl with dark black eyes. Rhoda was just such a person as could delight the hypercritical eyes of 'Madira. Negotiations complete, the wedding date was set. Everyone who knew 'Madira and her devoted son declared that they were very fortunate to attract another young woman. And they hinted this to Rhoda whenever they spoke to her about it.

Came the day of the wedding. The bells rang lustily. The grey morning mist dissolved in the heat of the sun to give way for jubilation. Everybody whispered that the day was a fitting one for a wedding on such a grand scale, and smiled ominously. Eleven o'clock struck, the time set for the start. The church building was packed with well-wishers and young women who go to a wedding to look at the trousseau and pass final if arbitrary judgment. The minister was waiting. The groom arrived. There was palpable breathless expectation in the air.

Her car must be late ... A shoe must be missing ... Some pins are probably being looked for ... She may be unwell and waiting for a nurse ... Oh well, a wedding without some hitch or misfortune is no good omen for a happy married life, is it? ... Eleven thirty, eleven forty-five ... A loud murmur was heard at the door. There she is, thought the groom, wiping a few beads of sweat from his forehead; it *must* be Rhoda; she was totally well only last night ... Many people thought many things ... No one appeared at the door. A shattering hiss ran through the rows of people.

Old ladies with good old hearts turned to look at one another and whispered. 'I dreamt about worms last night, and something bad always happens when I have dreamt about worms,' said one. 'I told you last week,' another said, 'that if nothing bad happens during this wedding, we'll all go to heaven.' Yet another ventured, 'God knows best, but Joel was never meant for that sweet girl.'

The minister, basically a stolid gentleman and, besides, being used to such delays at weddings and baptisms, was at first patient. But even he began to fret.

There was a hum and word went around that the bride was on the way. Sighs of relief were heard. People strained their necks to look about.

Twelve o'clock! There were increasing whispers. No bride! Someone was sent to enquire. He learnt from the bridal party that Rhoda had gone into a car and asked the driver to drive off, but not in the direction of the church.

'Ah, she has escaped,' said Joel. 'We might have known she would do this, mother! I am ruined!' He sat on the steps, feeling limp and tired. His mother was already talking to some of the people who had begun to file out.

Joel was a broken man. He laid his head on his mother's lap and cried like a child who has lost his best toy.

'Come, come, my son. This world can be a paradise, and it can be hell. But we must not give in so.'

The Woman Walks Out

One day 'Madira startled her neighbours by saying that she desired to be buried at Croesus Cemetery when she died, not at Nancefield, which was still new and covered with coarse grass. Croesus Cemetery was an old place but well-kept, dissected by avenues of evergreen trees. Here, graves that had no tombstones lay snug in the reflected glory of statuettes and tombstones that stood poised between memory and forgetfulness . . .

'Madira also undertook to sew her shroud and other drapery with which the dead are flattered for the last time. Whoever heard of a person making all this for the day death should visit her, as though a funeral were a wedding? The people were horrified and regarded it as the limit of eccentricity.

But then 'Madira, as she was known to everybody in the township, often startled people on the subject of death and funerals. On Sunday afternoons she slung her shawl over her shoulder, and with long strides she went down or up the street to visit friends. She propounded one theory and another and laid down the law on a number of other things, like the disciplining of a daughter-in-law, untidy married women, henpecked husbands.

'Give your man or woman a good coffin,' she said, 'made of brown shining wood, with full names on it. Drop the dead gently into the grave. It is the last thing you will ever be able to do for them on this earth.' She would go on to deplore the practice of the government of burying prisoners in sacking. She insisted that a dead body must be on view for all to see for the last time before it is buried.

'And people must not rob the dead man of his moment of final glory by speaking so much at the grave-side and in church. People then want to know who spoke best; who preached; who read the last words over the dead, who were there, and many other things except those about the dead. They forget all about the peaceful picture of a person lying with arms crossed, a head full of beautiful flowers, eyes and ears closed to all the useless and passing show of this rough world. Now, why shout over his grave? Why tell so many lies about him, things you were afraid or too proud to say about him when he lived? Give him his last chance. The man must be king, the woman must be queen for the last time. Before the white man came we never used to speak upon the dead: we just wept and buried them.' 'Madira would look round as if she were instructing people in a burial course.

'But the tea? Ugh! I never drink tea at any funeral lunch. They brew tea badly at funerals; always weak and cold. I do not understand why people are so bad at making tea.' Then she would look away with disgust.

The woman fell ill; seriously ill. Doctors from the

clinic came and went; prayer women came and went. Still her chest seemed to rebel against its owner. Her cough rent the air as if the breastplate would soon blow up like a lid off a pot when boiling porridge, or when steam rises.

Later 'Madira would not have any prayer-women come to her house except as mere visitors. 'Fools!' she cried out to Joel, her son, who was always at her sick-bed when he was not at work in town. 'Fools!' she repeated, 'they come here and pray to God to take my life if He so wills; or to let me live if He so wills — anything to free me from pain. Why give God a choice, why make Him think it would please them either way? Now, Joel, you see the evil hearts of these women! They want me to die! Oh, God!'

'Yes, Mamma,' said Joel.

She sat up, as one would do normally when getting out of bed in the morning. The exertion plunged her into a long fit of coughing.

'I will not die! I do not want to die, because others want me to die. By God, I must not die!' She was exhausted.

'Yes, Mamma,' said Joel. He had never been heard to say, 'No, Mamma', to contradict her. Joel also knew that whenever his mother sensed the slightest breeze of human feeling going against her will or wish, she bristled her hairs in order to assert herself; and he knew better than to try to curb her resistance, real or imaginary.

'Joel, if God should remember me, the shroud, the gown, are in my box. Make sure — make sure — the moth killer is still — is still in there. When the angel blows his trumpet on the Last Day — I shall — I shall be ready.' Her face was ghastly as she panted heavily. 'Put a tombstone over my grave, Joel,' the woman continued hastily, 'and I shall rest in peace when these things have been done.'

There was something horridly mysterious on her face which the simple mind of Joel could not fathom.

'Joel, last night — last night — I saw the face — the face of Death. The ugliness — the ugliness on that face — now makes me feel all the more — the more that I — I do not want to die. Keep those prayer women out, do — do you hear?'

'Yes, Mamma.'

The pastor was intending to go and pray for 'Madira 'out of mere Christian charity', as he told himself and others. But when he heard he might be snubbed he changed his mind. And he was glad and sorry all at once.

It seemed that the breach between him and 'Madira would never heal. It had started when 'Madira refused to apologize to the pastor and two prayer women for 'insulting' them. At a prayer meeting one Thursday — the day it was 'Madira's turn to preach — she had fixed her eyes on the two women among the audience during a whole sermon against witchcraft. The two women had reported the matter to the pastor. 'She was telling the other women that we are witches,' they had said. Nothing could convince them that 'Madira might not have been referring to them. 'Madira had laughed the whole idea off; which unsettled the pastor, because he himself had tried in vain to avoid holding court over such a trivial matter.

'All right, mothers,' he had said. 'I shall speak with my sister here.' They left, most disgruntled.

'I've had many complaints against you, sister.'

'Want to cut me out of the church?'

'No, no, no, of course not. I merely want to help. You see, you have a great deal of influence in the

Prayer Women's Guild, and whatever you say is taken very seriously.'

'Meaning what, Pastor?'

'That you must be careful what you say.'

'Madira had always sensed a sneaking glow of envy in the pastor's eyes, because she was so eloquent at church meetings and women's conferences.

'Will the Pastor please give me a letter of transfer?'

'But we want you, sister, you must keep our Guild alive.'

'I've made up my mind, Pastor, to go to another church.'

The pastor had paused and fidgeted with some papers, considering whether he should take advantage of the offer or remain forever saddled with what he regarded as 'Madira's domineering habits. He had written the transfer note. 'Go in peace, sister, and may God guide you.'

The woman had gone to the door, hesitated before opening it, then she reached out for the knob. After she had opened it, she turned round, adjusting her shawl and stood on the threshold. Standing there, so tall and upright, the sinews of her hands and her neck and sandalled feet seemed to pull tighter, co-ordinating in an effort to maintain the symmetry of the body for just that one moment.

'I've changed my mind,' 'Madira had said decisively. 'I'll stay in St Luke's. I like it here.' Then she had handed back the paper . . .

By sheer self-will 'Madira survived her illness, and was up again. But people nodded with understanding when they told one another that the old woman could not die because 'it wasn't her time yet'.

She left the township of tin-and-timber shacks to visit relatives in a country village some eighty miles away. 'Oh,' she said with a sigh when she explained the reason for going away, 'the white man has brought these diseases upon us, and then he cannot cure us of them!'

She was taking a walk in the fields one day when she collapsed, and was found unconscious by a white farmer's herdboy. He went to summon help in the neighbouring village but while he was away, 'Mdira died.

'Death is a thief,' says the African. When the trousseau she had prepared for the day of her wedding with death was very far away, the groom arrived.

Joel brought the drapery with him, but the simple country folk would not think of using it, even though they often like to satisfy the wishes of the dying.

'What will people say?'

'What miracle does your mother want us to perform?'

'It is madness — oh, the Lord forgive me, but . . . '

'I swear by my father who lies in peace yonder, the spirits will destroy us if we use her drapery . . . '

Croesus Cemetery was a long way off. 'Madira was buried in a most humble village graveyard where not a tombstone is to be seen, and where, among other things, thorn trees and ant-eaten wooden crosses tell a story of abject poverty.

Dinner at Eight

On a certain Monday it became frightfully important for two people to meet. Miss Pringle, because she had grown fond of Mzondi and pitied him immensely; Mzondi, for some other reason.

Miss Pringle made a conscious effort to win non-white friends, towards which end she wore an eternal smile on her lips. Mzondi disliked her in silence. Or maybe he thought he did, simply because he had come to loathe white people in authority. And he couldn't divorce the idea of white people from the idea of authority.

At 8 o'clock on Monday morning Miss Pringle called Mzondi to her office. 'Do come out to my flat this evening, Mzondi, I'd so much love a chat with you. I can see there's something worrying your mind. Tell me all about it when we're alone. Maybe I can help you.'

'I can't, madam. I ... I ... '

'Sit down, will you?'

'No thanks, madam.' He adjusted the crutch under his armpit as if to make a stand to protect his honour.

'Aren't you going to change your mind this fifth time — and come?'

'I can't . . . ' Won't this white woman realise I want none of her friendship? he thought.

'What's the matter with you black people? Trouble with you is you all feel and think you aren't as good as white people, or better. Other people trample on you because you're willing to become doormats . . . ' She suddenly realised that Mzondi didn't understand a thing she was saying.

'Come — do come, for my sake if not for yours,' she said lamely. 'Pick you up in my car at the hostel. Seven o'clock — all right? We can have supper at eight or so.' Mzondi was resisting, thinking: why does she bother me so!

'Only last week I had a few "coloured" friends, and next Wednesday I'm expecting other African friends.'

He continued to stand upright on his crutch, like a snake that remains cold in the warmest sun, but is prepared to strike to defend itself.

'All right, Mzondi, think about it and tell me yes or no after lunch time, eh? You may go back to your work now.'

It stung her to think that she, daughter of an upright pastor, a woman who liked a crowd of Blacks hovering over her admiringly — that she was being snubbed by a helpless cripple like Mzondi, a man who should grab the hand of friendship immediately it's extended.

Miss Pringle had been imported from the Cape Peninsula to run the Sheltered Employment Depot. Mzondi was one of the inmates. This private workshop took in incurable cripples to train them in some trade. She moved from one institution to another and carried a number of testimonials describing her as a person with 'an expert knowledge of the Native'; 'abundant sympathy for the needy'; 'a charming personality'; 'a pleasant disposition', etc. Sometimes a prospective employer asked for 'confidential' information about her. Often it was: 'a trifle tiresome, but hard-working'; 'a little overbearing, but conscientious'; or 'a likeable person, but a queer fish'. When she herself gave confidential information about people she knew, Miss Pringle used the same 'buts' and 'howevers'.

She liked to say to her cronies: 'My knowledge of the African . . . ' or 'after working with Africans for many years . . . ' or 'when I led a deputation to the Minister . . . ' 'Take Mzondi, for instance — I mean one of my inmates — so distrustful, so deep. But he's helpless, poor soul. Only about two or three months to live. I wonder who assaulted him so badly? What? Oh yes, the hospital doctor sent a report on him. No, nothing said about the nature of the assault — more than "head injuries". Telling me! — Paralysed him. If ever I should be battered on the head I don't want to live to suffer like him . . . No relatives, no address — one of those people who come from nowhere, and pass on to nowhere . . . My heart bleeds for him. I wonder if he feels his life hurrying to an end . . . Oh no, not the only one at my depot . . . Naturally they aren't told about it, you know. Poor dears . . . Not a bit — all my life I've been helping Africans . . . Thankless job? Doesn't matter really. Knowing you've done a good job is satisfying enough, you know. So much more fun working with blacks than whites, anyhow. Too independent — that's the way with whites . . . '

Miss Pringle toyed with a ballpoint pen after Mzondi had left her office. Since that doctor's report

came three days back, it had become a passion with
her to befriend Mzondi. The black man sensed it
whenever she bent over him to show him how to
operate the new machine. He resented this behaviour.
She, on the other hand, didn't know why similar
reports about other inmates hadn't affected her as
much as Mzondi's.

The point of the pen clicked back and forth. She
could almost see Mzondi sitting in his usual corner,
shoulders hunched as he bent over his knitting
machine. Lopsided body: what lurked in there? He
bore his handicap with irresistible cheek. Pathetic
beautiful lips: why did they say so little? Steady eyes,
almost expressionless. The paralysed flank of his
body looked as if it might cave in at any moment and
bring flesh and bones down to the ground in dis-
mantled pieces.

Mzondi was also thinking of Miss Pringle, of his
ever-tired bones, his withering flesh, the gong that
echoed in his head, more often now. That beating-up
he had had from prison boys — fellow-prisoners — at
Number Four. Savage. Several times they had kicked
Mzondi on the head. The warder standing there,
shouting to him to tell him where he had hidden the
£3 000 payroll they said he had snatched away with a
friend. And crying out repeatedly: 'I don't know,
baas, I don't know, baas. Please don't let them kill
me, baas, I don't have it, baas.' The warder had
threatened, persuaded, cursed, commanded. He had
ordered the boys to 'hell him up some more'; and
they had liked it.

The police had caught up with Mzondi after killing
his friend during that manhunt. But he had already
hidden the money in the district of Heidelberg — not
the payroll — £200 they had earned from illicit

liquor-brewing. He had been handcuffed and assaulted by the police. 'If you show us where you hid the cash, boy, we'll give you some of it,' one of them had suggested. He wouldn't tell. He couldn't tell. They would never have believed him. And then those hellish days at Number Four, awaiting trial.

In court Mzondi had denied all knowledge of the money or his friend. None of the victims of the robbery could identify him. State witnesses lied. The warder, for instance, had said in court that Mzondi had told him he had hidden the money where no other living soul could find it. Ignoring the interpreter, Mzondi had shouted: 'This man lies, sir!' and paused, looking appealingly up to the magistrate. 'That's the man who got prisoners to beat me up to force me to tell him where the money was. It's true, sir, I swear by my ancestors who sleep in their graves . . . !'

'Silence!' the magistrate had shouted. 'Tell the accused I shan't tolerate such contempt. He must behave himself. Ask him why he didn't report the assault immediately.'

'I reported it, sir, but the police refused to write it down. They said I was mad.'

'I've no reason to disbelieve the warder's evidence about what you are supposed to have said to him, nor have I any reason to doubt that a man in such a responsible position could be telling the truth when he says he didn't assault you.'

Through the interpreter Mzondi said calmly — as if to himself — 'They told me in jail that I was wasting my time reporting the warder to the police.'

He hardly heard the magistrate pronounce his acquittal. He barely heard: 'The State witnesses have been lying and they have pointed out different

persons at the identification parade.' His acquittal
didn't seem to matter half so much as the failure of
the law to punish the men who had crippled him for
life.

He had been sent back to hospital for further
treatment.

And now, here he was in a sheltered employment
depot. Paralysed, useless, Mzondi reflected, choking
with a lump of agony — with two hundred pounds
hidden somewhere in the Heidelberg district, waiting
for the day he would fetch it and rent a beautiful
house and bring a fat little nine-year-old girl up from
Eshowe — his daughter. Her mother had died when
she was born.

He was thinking about all this when he turned
round to see a policeman come in, walk to the door
of Miss Pringle's office and knock. Instinctively he
grabbed his crutch, raised it like a man wading
through a river in flood, and lowered it again,
realising that he didn't want to stand up. The
constable had gone into the office. After a few
minutes he and Miss Pringle appeared at the door.
They stood for a few seconds. Miss Pringle seemed to
point in Mzondi's direction: the constable looked and
nodded his head and went out. If Miss Pringle had
known what Mzondi was thinking, she would have
told him that the policeman had come about a
burglary that had occurred the previous night at the
depot.

She knows, she knows, Mzondi mumbled to himself. They both want to get at my money! Smiles,
friendly smiles, friendly invitations . . . to get me
drunk and then drag my secret out of me!

He got up and went to Miss Pringle's office. 'Yes,
I'll be happy to come to your flat tonight. Yes,

tonight.' Miss Pringle only casually sensed a constriction in Mzondi's voice. What she could not see was the fact that it had become frightfully important for Mzondi to visit her flat. Nor did she hear the bell that gonged in the man's brain: tonight's appointment, appointment for tonight!

What did the policeman want, someone next to Mzondi wanted to know. Do you ever ask what a cockroach wants when you see it run across your floor, a hunchback replied. Mzondi thought: *Cockroaches, hell. Don't you see he wants me!* Sit down without legs — another chimed in with a sandy voice — there's a cop lighting a fire under you; walk on two legs, there's a cop wanting to freeze them; walk on one leg, a cop trips you up — why?

Hide two hundred pounds and . . .

The hunchback's voice towered above the others: stay crippled and be happy with dung in your gizzard. And the babbling went on . . . My father was once rich, said the hunchback. Very rich. If you saw his cattle on a hill, they were like trees.

Two hundred pounds a passing wind! Tonight, tonight, damn you all! The gong went on beating in his brain.

When is the bell going to ring for stopping work? And someone else: There's a party at Ma-Shelabi's, you know!

Want to trap me, do you? We'll see about that. Those days of the chase: that night he struggled through a bog, the police giving chase, somewhere miles behind. His friend too tired to go further, urging him to move on . . . *He shouldn't have tried to break at the last minute. Those cops are trigger-happy.* He remembered newspapers' screaming head-lines about one of the biggest manhunts in South

African crime history. Smell of blood at Number
Four.

The babble in the workshop went on. Ar-r-r, this
wretched leg! Look, you leg, the day I have you cut
off, you'll be sorry for losing me! I'll have you
chucked to the worms for a meal!

Tonight.

Seven o'clock. Miss Pringle and Mzondi were on
their way to a Hillbrow flat; Miss Pringle's. They used
the basement lift for 'Natives, goods and hawkers'.
They didn't see the watchman go to a telephone
booth after he had greeted them.

About two minutes later, two people who most
wanted to see each other in a place where they
wouldn't be interfered with, sat facing each other in
Miss Pringle's flat on the fourth floor. How beautiful
and helpless he looks, she thought. 'What'll you have
for a drink?' After listening to the repertoire he said
'Sherry'.

He put his hand into the inside coat pocket to feel
a hard metal object. *After the sherry,* he thought:
soon, quick!

She went up to the window and peeped out. No,
there was nobody there tonight. None of the boys
from Hospital Hill police station, who she knew
haunted the corridors or the pavement opposite.
They knew she entertained non-whites, and they
thought they were giving her a gracious length of
rope, sure that one day they'd clamp down on her
and her black partner in the middle of an 'immoral
act'. Lately they'd been peering through bedroom
windows and hiding behind wardrobes, to catch their
victims in the act.

'Poor boys,' she heard herself saying, 'they can't
think of friendship between male and female without

pillows and blankets. No one across there, anyhow.'

'Who are those?'

'Ugh, just thinking out aloud. No one of importance. Tell me about yourself. Where you were born, your parents, all that.'

She's lying. She was giving the policeman a signal, dirty dog! He took a firmer grip of his crutch. He made as if to stand, and slumped back again.

'Please, Miss Pringle. Would you — would you rub this useless knee first, then I'll tell you something. This leg's going to be the death of me, if it keeps aching like this.'

'Of course!' She went hurriedly over to him. She was on her knees, bending over his leg. Suddenly he raised the crutch and, with his strong arm, he struck her on the back of the head. Her legs sagged and slowly she slumped to the floor. He struck her again, then looked around, panting. He stood up with difficulty, and made for the door. Quickly, he switched off the light, pulled out the key and locked the door from the outside. After pulling the key out again he stepped onto the landing. He hobbled to the lift, breathing heavily after those quick violent movements.

In the basement Mzondi lingered in a dark corner. Just as well, because a white constable stood there in the light talking to the night watchman. He waited until the white man had shot up in the lift, dug his hand into one of his pockets and extracted a fiver. Then he walked straight to the watchman, who stared at him stolidly.

'Take this and sew your lips together. I'm not talking English when I say there's more for you if your tongue never moves to tell anyone you saw me tonight!'

'You're talking Zulu, brother!' the watchman said slowly, and moved away from that part of the building for the rest of the night. He fingered the ten shilling note he had received from the constable and the fiver with satisfaction.

Two hundred pounds. A clean house. Eshowe. The cavernous gonging.

Up there on the fourth floor the young constable waited outside Miss Pringle's door. He thought of how he was going to thrill the boys with the news of his discovery. He'd tell them, slowly, how he had entered, ordered the couple to get out of bed and watched them dress . . .

He inserted his duplicate key and entered noisily. *'Hemel!'* he gasped and stared at the mess that was Miss Pringle's head.

The constable only seemed to recover from his daze when he blew on his whistle out in the street. He broke into a trot towards the railway station, his mind a jumble of things he'd tell the sergeant. Such a white bitch — served her right, he kept saying aloud. Hell, that promotion's busted up now . . . !

Mzondi heard the whistle. After exerting himself a few more hundred yards, he took cover against a huge tree on the brow of a gradual slope leading to the railway line. He huddled close, breathing as heavily as ever, his heart behaving like a hundred pistons. The clock had just chimed eight when he saw the policeman in the glare of a fluorescent street lamp, still blowing his whistle. The black man took out his gun and aimed to shoot. He was about to pull the trigger, pointing the gun at the constable's stomach when he came to a stop, facing the tree. Then a sharp streak of pain raced up his paralysed side and his hand trembled. He lowered the gun. The policeman passed on.

He tried to think what he had done and what had come over him since eight in the morning, when Miss Pringle had called him to the office. But something inside him was sagging lower and lower. He felt he didn't care about what had happened. He wanted to rest — without moving any organ of his body. *Two hundred pounds!* Then it was that he felt a dark cloud cover him.

In the early hours of the morning they found his body. His arms embraced the trunk of the tree. There was nothing on him to tell who he was or where he was from. The only thing of importance that could be linked up with Mzondi was the murder of Miss Pringle.

Man Must Live

First stop Mayfair, Langlaagte, Ikona Westbury, Newclare, Randfontein train! Randfontein train: *i-kona* Westbury, Newclare, first stop Mayfair, Langlaagte, Maraisburg, Roodepoort; all stations Randfontein! *Uyaphi? Nkosi yam?* (Where are you going to? — My Lord!)

Khalima Zungu's voice echoed through the station platform and in the subways. Masses of people rushed into the train. Khalima Zungu was a railway policeman. He was proud of it too. So he enjoyed reciting the names of stations and sidings off pat without giving them much thought.

He had a good thundering voice too, and was pleased it was of great use here. In fact, many people said he could make an outstandingly good baritone singer. Now this did not impress him much; he did not know much about singers and singing anyhow. But what did impress him was that it was also from *women*, this remark, and if *women* said it, it must be a compliment! Not that he was so conceited, but Zungu clearly had a wholesome respect for anything that a woman said. Sometimes, of course, he had to admit, more than he liked to, that it was a weakness rather than a virtue.

Khalima Zungu also overheard such remarks as: 'Isn't he fine in that uniform; look at his broad shoulders and his big strong hands!' 'God does give some people good, big and tall bodies!' Zungu did not understand where God came in, but women had said this; so why wonder? He had good reason to be proud of himself and his work.

He had masses of people under his control. He paced up and down the platform to see his charges onto the train. Now he would say a harsh word or two, shout at someone at the other end, then he would drag a small boy out of the crowd to save him from harm.

They were so much like cattle, some of them, he thought; not unlike those cattle he looked after when a boy in Zululand, where he had once saved a girl who was overtaken by the stampeding herd. Most of them, he admitted, were simply anxious to get home after a day's hard work to enjoy the luxury of homely relaxation.

But why, even if this argument held good, should a man sometimes go into a wrong train and then ask from inside if the train was going to Orlando or Pimville or some other place? Many of this species, he reflected were often carried away by wrong trains, or the trains carried wrong passengers, whichever way you liked to put it.

Zungu also knew that he had to put up with people who left the right train and followed another crowd dashing to a train at the opposite platform, and perhaps fell back with them like waves beating blindly against a rocky shore and splashing back. So much like sheep some of them were, my Lord!

But he could not help feeling he was equal to the situations, although the more he thought of them the more contemptuous he felt for these two-legged sheep. Sometimes Zungu felt sympathetic towards them for their ignorance, but when people behaved like this despite the fact that the Railway Administration employed Khalima Zungu to assist them (which he tried to do) then surely, he thought, he was entitled to despise their lack of intelligence.

This afternoon, particularly, as he paced to and fro amidst the thick crowds of people waiting for their trains, Zungu was highly pleased with himself. He had just told a woman who had enquired from him that the Cape Town train would leave at 10.10 that night from platform number one. He wondered if he had put enough music in that 'ten ten' and if he had swung his left arm gracefully enough to look at his watch before supplying the valuable information. But he convinced himself he must have provided the desired touch.

The woman had thanked him in a not unpleasant voice that left a smile lingering on her mouth. My Lord — what would such people do without obliging Khalima Zungu! He decided this afternoon that he liked this work, what with all the nice remarks and how-nice-of-you smiles.

Khalima Zungu always reminded himself he had worked his way up through his own initiative. At the age of fifteen he had run away from the little village in the heart of Zululand where he had attended a small school.

Before passing Standard VI he had openly told his guardian (he was an orphan) that he did not want to attend school any more. His reasons were that he was grown up, he could read and write, and if so much of life could be learned out of books, as his teacher had often impressed upon his mind, then practical problems of life could surely teach him a hundred times more than books.

Khalima Zungu had worked in Natal for his train fare to Johannesburg. He obtained a job as a store-man in a wholesale clothing factory, where he loaded and off-loaded bundles and bales of material as they came in and out. After five years in factory work he landed in the building trade as one of the hands in bricklaying. He remembered with pride how he was made foreman over the non-European workers. Zungu also remembered how much he enjoyed moving from one suburb to another.

That was the way to learn about life and living. You had to know how to catch three or four bricks thrown to you at a time; you had to turn a spade dexterously this way and that in mixing cement and sand; you had to throw earth, with precision, in almost one lump onto a lorry. When Zungu was raised to the rank of foreman he felt more than ever before that he hated book-learning.

When the sixth year elapsed Zungu decided he needed a change. Soon he found work with a road-building contractor. He knew he had to start from the beginning again, but that was as it should be. He told himself he was no novice in handling a pick or shovel. They went over miles and miles of highway, from town to city, from city to town, from town to 'dorp'.

The eighth year found Zungu still splashing sparks out of rock with a pick, flattening out concrete and tar on roads. He still loved the sound of the pick as it went 'zip' into the earth. It seemed to give a more majestic sound when it went in to the accompaniment of his 'jeep'. He loved the sound of the pick as it struck rock with a 'twing'.

Zungu was compact and muscular. He had stamina at which even his fellow-workers and employer marvelled. It always took a long time before he sweated and when a bead of sweat rolled down his temple, he knew his muscles were proving their worth.

At this point the primitive man in him seemed to be stirred. He cried for more outlet, and then looked a brute as he whacked the pick against hard ground and drove the shovel through earth and stones. It was no wonder that he was made foreman in his third year on the road.

Zungu knew that most of the workers under him disliked him. They murmured complaints among themselves that he was 'driving them like oxen'. Some even went so far as to say that he was only strong in appearance but weak and cowardly within. They said he showed this in the way he cringed before his employer and the European workers to seek their favour.

'It's strange, you know,' he overheard one saying to a group of listeners during the rest hour, 'why is it that our people respect and fear the word of a white man and do not show either for their fellow-men?' 'Why should a person be one man towards his employer and be a totally different man towards those who rub shoulders with him?' another asked.

He always remembered this as the one outstanding occasion when he became very furious but mastered his anger. He remembered how he had sneered at them inwardly after listening. But why had he not embarrassed them by suddenly appearing on the scene and smashing the jaws of the gossipers so that they had a more important thing to complain about? He could not answer this question. Instead he had only sneered at them inwardly and told himself that he, Khalima Zungu, had helped construct highways for the comfort of mankind and would not defile his noble hands on the jaws of a couple of weak good-for-nothing boys like these. Even more important than this, he told himself, was the fact that man must live.

Yes, man must live. Zungu had nursed this philosophy of life since he left the village school in Zululand. Let men accuse, deride and ridicule you in your actions; let them complain that you don't respect or fear them; let them say you don't earn your living honestly; but they too, sooner or later, will come down to the hard, cold and indisputable fact that man must live.

That night Zungu was relaxing after the tiring heat of the rush hours in the afternoon. Even then he was not admitting that he was tired — that is, to the degree measured according to his own standard when he used to work on the road. He was only enjoying the night breeze in the quiet of the station. Zungu's thoughts were careering smoothly in his mind. He could not have been more satisfied and happier than now. He was doing well, he told himself, in the fourth year of his service with the Railway Administration. He had learned much during the past years.

Khalima Zungu had dealt with rock and sand and iron before; he had to deal with life now. If you could have a strong hold of a pick and crush stone to powder, there was no reason why you should not be able to shout at people to get into a train to Pimville instead of to Germiston if they wanted to go to Pimville.

It was even comparatively easy here, he thought; you could handle a man by the scruff of the neck and bring him down to implicit obedience, but to work at a tall building or have a pick chafe blisters out of your hand was not so easy.

He had seen people of vastly varying characteristics, many of whom had conjured up some crude impressions in his mind.

Only today, for instance, he had seen a man and a woman, evidently his wife, who was much larger than her partner. The way she talked and looked at him made Zungu guess that he was henpecked — the kind he had sometimes seen thrown over a fence by a woman, or locked out of the house if he had failed to carry out her instructions to her satisfaction.

Then there was the man with a hump on his back. What burdens time and space sometimes picked on one to carry, just because a man did not know he *must* live! Probably, for all Zungu knew, this might just have been one of that odd and queer section of the human race that seem to have been created expressly to amuse the rest; the type that give beggars all they have and then resort to begging themselves, with only one monument of good service — a hump!

My Lord — what afflictions the white people have brought upon us! Now, how could a man in the days of our forefathers be bald-headed in the twenties or thirties if he was sound in the brain? Surely that bald-headed man he had seen was hardly out of the thirties. How on earth could he even be impudent enough to talk to him, Khalima Zungu, a member of the Railway Police Force, as though he was facing an equal? Perhaps, he remembered thinking, the man was trying to feel inwardly big to conceal his ridiculous shortness of stature and his premature baldness.

Such fools should be suffered to preserve one's own dignity. Anyway, he had no time for the class, to which this one apparently belonged, that reads so much, and knows so little how to live.

Many more Zungu had seen: the long-faced stringy woman who seemed to be engaged in an eternal war with herself; the little boy who scurried away under his mother's shawl at the sight of him (even children recognised his greatness!); the round fat man with folds in the nape of his neck, who threaded his way through the clustering crowds of people as if he were a toy that had been wound and set going in a bee line in spite of all in its way. Money-minded people usually walked this way, Zungu thought. Of course they wanted to live, he admitted, like he did. But such people usually died in pursuit of life, long before they started to live. Or he might even have been the sort that was brought up softly and that frittered away their time wielding tennis racquets or jerking their bodies in funny movements in dance halls to weird noises! Just soft people who were not any the better for their knowledge of a world of things.

Yet if they must live, let them; all these particles of a world that scattered with the onset of night and would re-assemble tomorrow and tomorrow, each day forming an organised bundle of unlike disorganised parts — a world on Park Station.

Khalima Zungu gradually realised something must be found to help fulfil his purpose to live. Until now he had not thought seriously about marriage. He had once or twice fallen in love, but he was naturally girl-shy, although he respected a woman's word. So these incidents were of a passing nature. And he always excused his girl-shyness by telling himself a woman was not yet necessary in his life project. He could live quite gaily without partnership with the female of the species. He did not necessarily deny the importance of the physical side of such partnership. In fact, if he must live, he thought, this could not be overlooked. And after all, he was just as much entitled to his ancestors' heritage as the next man was to his own.

But Zungu now thought and wished someone might meet him half-way, some woman he could win without having to exert so much effort to overcome his shyness. He knew he stood very little chance of such luck, but he hoped. Those women who had come into his life before did not satisfy the requirements of his standard of an ideal wife, the wife of his dreams and imagination . . .

One very cold mid-July night Khalima Zungu paced about on Platform Number Ten. His hands were deep in his coat pockets, his ears buried under the lapels. One could hardly see his face under the peak of his cap, drawn well down. He looked up at the big railway clock. He did not feel disposed to take his hands out of his pockets. It was five minutes to twelve.

The last train to Randfontein must be pulling in now. Zungu was thinking it was late when he saw it sliding in effortlessly, if somewhat cautiously. There was only one person entering and two or three getting out, so the train did not stop long. It had scarcely disappeared when a lady came towards him, panting. She stopped abruptly and gave a sigh of despair when she looked at the back of the train disappearing.

Zungu approached the woman, feeling somewhat sympathetic. 'I hope you are not from far, because if so, you have no luck; that is the last train. No other till 3.15 in the morning.'

She heaved another sigh of despair. 'I am from

Inanda, and can't go back now; no use, I'll just have to sit here until 3.15.'

'You are not allowed to sit here at this time,' Zungu said primly. He was dealing with a lady, but rules were rules.

'But I know nobody near here; where shall I go to?'

'I wish I knew; that's what I would like to ask you,' he replied not without sarcasm. He looked at her appealing face, then at her whole figure with a searching hard stare in his eyes. 'Em — an expensive coat, likely the rich type of woman who felt so independent that she could move about at this time of night . . . 'Em — not unattractive though . . .

Zungu thought for a moment of what he could do. It was not really his job, but he was human. An idea struck him. It would be against the rules, but it could be risked. You could always explain things if questioned afterwards. Besides, if the woman continued staring at him in this can't-you-do-something manner, there was no saying how long she might do so, and neither he nor she could afford to look at each other indefinitely in such cold weather.

He told her what he could do and she accepted the offer. They went up the stairs to his little waiting room, where a fire was blazing happily and enticingly. She sat down with eagerness and decided that she was going to like it here, and that the little fears she had begun to have when he had suggested this scheme to her were unfounded.

They soon found themselves sailing on the glassy sea of easy conversation. She was a Mosotho, but could speak Zulu fluently. Khalima Zungu soon learned her name — Mrs Sophia Masite; that she was a widow, had two sons and a daughter; that they all lived with her in Randfontein. They talked about many other things.

Ten minutes past three found the two walking down the steps to the train. After the train had left Zungu went back to his fire. The crackling sound of the fire, the sound of the flames dancing happily and greedily licking the roof of the grate, the radiating gentle warmth, all these, were in tune with his inner emotions. They told him life was like the magic carpet he had read of in school. It carried you over mountain peaks, over green valleys and beautiful streams; through fearfully dark gorges and over rugged ugly boulders; over sharp unfriendly briars, through jungles and dark mysterious kingdoms, where you felt you were being swallowed up into the pit of death; and again you could emerge into the smiling world, swim in the fragrant smell of flowers, taste of the sweet, the bitter and the bitter-sweet fruit; always and for ever borne by the magic carpet — whither no one knew. Yet, whatever the end, man must live.

Zungu also felt that the hollowness, emptiness and the vague sense of defeatism that sometimes overwhelmed him were not there. The smiling face of that woman, all genuine thankfulness and obvious admiration written on it, and her gentle and communicative voice filled him with the sense of the beauty of life. And he knew the magic carpet had brought him to this stage.

A week later Zungu received a card from Mrs Masite, inviting him to a party on the occasion of her daughter's twentieth birthday. He was clearly excited and determined not to miss it.

That party was the turning point of Khalima Zungu's life. He was now forty years of age and it was during the party that Zungu decided to master his shyness. It was a very easy task, when he came to think of it afterwards — this business of winning women.

Zungu and Mrs Masite were married three weeks later. She was a rich woman, as Zungu had judged on the night when she was a damsel in distress. They soon decided that he should not work any more. Even if he exhausted his savings, she told him, it was no matter; he could draw on hers, which made his look like the contents of a child's money box.

It did not take long before he started to draw on his wife's money. Things went smoothly at first between him and his wife and step-children. Zungu had no cause for discontent. It was a world of plenty and man must live, live abundantly.

But as time wore on and he was taking life for granted, the children began to show him that he, being no more than a step-father, was not entitled to their respect. Zungu tried to keep his feelings to himself. The climax came when one night his step-daughter told him unreservedly in the presence of her mother that he was 'backward', 'uncivilized', and 'conceited', and that, if he wanted to know the truth, her mother had married him out of pity because he had nothing to speak for him in trying to earn his living. So he must behave himself.

Zungu knew he had developed the habit of drinking excessively. He knew his nerves were giving way, and that easy life had begun to dull his wits. But he could not take it. Such insults as his step-daughter had hurled at him must not be repeated. In fact, they showed ill-breeding.

He looked knives at his step-daughter, then at her mother. She was unmoved. Was she sitting there indifferently and passively without a word of reproach to her daughter? There was an expression of contempt and derision on that face of hers. Her eyes dared him to talk. Zungu was about to say something after working up his fury to a high pitch, but to his disappointment he found he had nothing to say. Suddenly a sense of defeat and hollowness came upon him. He was tired. His brain was stagnant, his muscles limp, his spirit flat.

Of course, he, Khalima Zungu, formerly of the Railway Police Force, should have seen the motive behind this woman's subtle intrigues in dragging him into marriage. He now saw it, clear as crystal, that she had married him as a convenience. She had always remained in the background when her children insulted him. Most probably she was pulling the wire and conducting this machinery. He had been to her a humble, harmless and ideal companion. She now realized his value had ended where his drinking habit began. Zungu had a genuine love for his wife; of this he was sure.

In his magical world of riches and splendour Zungu had been used as a tool of vengeance by his wife. Much against his will, however much contempt he had for the so-called intelligentsia class, he had received them into the house and behaved as a gentleman should — as far as his limited knowledge allowed. Then there were the ordinary class, to which Zungu belonged. He had to refuse them admission because his wife said they had tried to stand in her way when she aspired for wealth and learning, out of sheer jealousy.

On a warm breezy night Khalima Zungu walked from the beer hall, drunk as a fiddler. He could barely support himself on his legs, but he managed to struggle up to the door of his house. He knocked, but nobody answered. Again he knocked, and again, but the door was not opened. He then tried the knob. It was locked. Zungu kicked and heaved his shoulders against the door until sweat ran down his face. Then he remembered he had a duplicate key which the locksmith had made for him to use on such nights as this when he was locked out.

He entered and roared out loudly, but the house was empty. Even in his state of mind Zungu could not but notice a difference. His mind struggled to diagnose the situation. Then he decided that there was no furniture, no pictures; in fact, nothing but the bare skeleton of the house. He went to the bedroom. Here he found only his case of clothes on the floor. Besides this sad tale the house could tell no more. Zungu fell on the floor and remained there, a hopeless heap.

At about midnight he woke up. He wondered where he was and why he was there and not on his bed. The light was still on. Then he remembered that the scenery was not new to him. As quick as lightning Zungu sprang to his feet. He rushed out at a speed not unlike that of a scalded cat to the outside storehouse. There was a drum of petrol, left as he thought, because it was of no use to that pack of foxes.

My Lord — he, Khalima Zungu, formerly of the Railway Police Force, would teach them a lesson. Take out all the yolk and white of an egg and mock him with the empty shell! He would reduce this shell to cinders if it meant cremating himself alive in it.

Zungu carried the drum into the house and poured its contents over the floor and splashed some over the walls. He set the house on fire. He stood quite still as the flames reached out for one another madly and hungrily. Then he remembered, strangely enough, what he had been told at school about hell. It must be like this in hell. The spectacle itself was hell incarnated, and here he was, fitting well into it as though he was the only evil-doer (if he was) worth burning in hell. But my Lord — he must live!

With this thought he dashed to where he imagined the door must be, but hit against a naked wall. He turned this way and that, choking with fumes and burning. Presently he found an exit and staggered onto the verandah. Zungu felt nauseated and felt himself falling into someone's arms . . .

When Zungu came to, he found himself in hospital. His mind was still hazy and misty. There were some people around his bed, whom he recognised as neighbours. One of them told him how he had found him, wrapped him up in some sacking and rolled him over the ground. He had known that if anybody was in that house it would most likely be Zungu himself, because he had seen his wife and children going away early in the day.

He was not seriously burnt, but the shock had been severe. Zungu recovered. When he left the hospital, the problem of where to sleep confronted him. The man who had saved him offered him temporary food and a sleeping place because he had a large family. Soon he realized he would have to be a nomad, a tramp, sleeping where he could, eating what he could get.

At the foot of a hill stands a corrugated iron shanty. Zungu put it up for himself. His experience in building stood him in good stead, although he admitted, not without a pang at the sense of Time's ironic twists, this experience was not accounting for itself at the right moment.

He can be seen going to and fro with a load on his

back, staggering with a stooping gait. That upright muscular stature has weathered in the test of time; that confident light stride has slowed down to heavy, uncertain and clumsy movement, giving him the appearance of a dog wounded after a hunt. Yet he is only in his forties.

That world of love and plenty was a dream world, when he thinks of it, whose glories have vanished with the dawn of reality. Today Zungu feels as if Time takes a slow pace purposely to lengthen his life, of which now remain a few rags, too worn out to be patched. He still drinks and murmurs to himself.

Zungu's eyes are expressionless, whether he be happy or not. That twinkle is gone. But there is something in that stolid blankness in those eyes; something of stubbornness. When he looks at you, you cannot help but read the stubborn words: What do you expect me to be — a magician or a superman, or a soft learned genteel animal? My Lord — I *must* live, man!

The Master of Doornvlei

The early summer rain was pouring down fiercely.

In the mud-and-grass church house a bird flitted from one rafter to another, trapped. All was silent in the church except for an occasional cough that punctuated the preacher's sermon. Now and then, to relieve the gravity of the devotional moment, a few members of the congregation allowed themselves to be ensnared by the circling movements of the bird.

But only a few of them. Most of the people had their eyes fixed on the elderly preacher, as if they were following the motion of every line on his lips as he gave his sermon. In any case, he did not have a booming voice like his deacon's (a point on which the old man was often plagued by a feeling of inferiority). So his listeners always watched his lips. One or two older women at the back screwed up their faces to see him better.

A nine-year-old boy was particularly charmed by the lost bird, and his eyes roved with it. Then he felt pity for it and wished he could catch it and let it out through the window which it missed several times.

But the preacher went on, and his listeners soared on the wings of his sermon to regions where there was no labour or sweat and care.

Suddenly the boy saw the bird make straight for a closed window and hit against the glass and flutter to the floor. It tried to fly but could not. He went to pick it up. He hugged it and stroked it. He looked about, but the people stared ahead, like stolid clay figures. Why are they so cold and quiet when a bird is in pain, he asked himself.

It lay quietly in his hand, and he could feel the slight beat of the heart in the little feathered form.

'And so, brothers and sisters,' the preacher concluded, 'the Holy Word bids us love one another, and do to others as we would that they do to us. Amen.' He asked his flock to kneel for prayer.

At this time Mfukeri, the foreman of Doornvlei Farm on which the makeshift church was built, came in. He looked around and spotted his target — a puny wisp of a boy with scraggy legs, the boy with the bird in his hand.

When he took the boy out the people continued to kneel, unperturbed, except for the raising of a head here and there, perhaps just to make sure who the victim was this time. As the two went out the boy's rather big waistcoat that dangled loosely from his shoulders, flapped about.

It was common for Mfukeri to butt in at a prayer session to fetch a man or woman or child for a job that needed urgent attention. The congregants were labour tenants, who in return for their work earned the few square yards of earth on which they lived, a ration of mealie-meal, sugar and an occasional piece of meat.

When they complained about such disturbances to

the farmer, Sarel Britz, he said: 'I'm just to my labourers. I favour nobody above the rest. Farm work is farm work; I often have to give up my church service myself.'

The boy tried to protect the bird. He could not keep it on his person, so he put it under a tin in the fowlrun before he went about the work Mfukeri had directed him to do. The rain continued to pour down.

The following day the boy took ill with pneumonia. He had got soaked in the rain. On such days the little mud-and-grass houses of the labourers looked wretched: as if they might cave in any time under some unseen load. The nearest hospital was some way off, and if the workers wanted to see the district surgeon, they would have to travel 25 miles there and back. The district surgeon could only be seen once a week.

The boy ran a high temperature. When he was able to speak he asked his mother to go and see how his bird fared in the fowlrun. She came back to tell him that the bird had been found under a tin, dead. That same night the boy died.

When the news went round, the workers seemed to run beserk.

'It has happened before . . . '

'My child — not even ten yet . . . !'

'Come, let's go to Sarel Britz . . . !'

'No, wait, he'll be angry with us, very angry . . . '

'We can also get angry . . . '

'Yes, but the white man is very powerful . . . '

'And truly so — where do we get work if he drives us off the farm . . . ?'

'He wants our hands and our sweat — he cannot do that . . . '

'He beats us, and now he wants to kill us . . . '

'Send him back to Rhodesia — this Mfukeri . . . !'

'Yes, we don't do such things on this farm . . . '

'By the spirits, we don't work tomorrow until we see this thing out . . . !'

'Give us our trek-passes . . . ! Save our children . . . !'

'Ho friends! I am not going with you. I have children to look after . . . !'

'That is why we are going to Sarel Britz . . . !'

'Come, friends, let's talk first before we march to the master of Doornvlei.'

Tau Rathebe, who could read and write, rallied the workers to an open spot not far from the main gate. Grim and rugged farm workers; shaggy; none with extra flesh on him; young and old, with tough sinewy limbs. Those who were too scared to join the march kept in the bushes nearby to watch. Women remained behind.

The men were angry and impatient. 'We want Mfukeri away from Doornvlei, or we go, trek-pass or none!' was the general cry, echoed and re-echoed.

And they marched, as they had never done before, to the master's house.

Britz and Mfukeri were standing on the front verandah, waiting. It was to be expected: the foreman had already gone to warn Britz. Apart from what knowledge he had about Tau Rathebe, it was plain since the early morning that the workers were not prepared to work.

'What is it, men?'

'The people want Mfukeri sent away,' said Tau. 'He has been using his sjambok on some workers, and now old Petrus Sechele's son is dead, because Mfukeri took him out in the rain. I've warned him about this before.'

'I'll think about it. You're asking me to do a difficult thing; you must give me time to think.'

'How long?' asked Tau.

Sarel Britz felt annoyed at the implied ultimatum and Tau's insolent manner; but he restrained himself.

'Till noon today. Just now I want you to go to your work. I'm just, and to show it, Mfukeri is not going to the fields until I've decided.'

They dispersed, each to his work, discontented and surly. When Mfukeri left Sarel Britz in conference with his mother, the foreman's face had lost its usual smooth and slippery sheen. He looked deflated and dejected.

'I've told him not to use the sjambok, but he insists on doing it, just because I forbid it,' said Britz when he had gone.

'Reason?' Marta Britz asked.

'Just to make me feel I depend on him.'

'He never behaved like this when your father was alive. Once he was told he must do a thing or mustn't, he obeyed.'

There was a pause during which mother and son almost heard one another's thoughts.

'You know, Mamma, when I was at university — on the experimental farm — I knew many black and 'coloured' folk. Thinking back on the time, now, makes me feel Pa was wrong.'

'Wrong about what?'

'About Kaffirs being children.'

'But they are, my son. Your father himself said so.'

'No, one has to be on the alert with them. One can't afford to take things for granted.'

'How are they grown up?'

Sarel went and stood right in front of her. 'Yes, Ma, they're fully grown up; some of them are cleverer and wiser than a lot of us whites. Their damned patience makes them all the more dangerous. Maybe Mfukeri's still somewhat of a child. But certainly not the others. Take today, for instance. A coming together like this has never been heard of on a white man's farm. And they've left everything in the hands of their leader. No disorder. They're serpents' eggs, and I'm going to crush them.' He paused.

'I didn't tell you that Mfukeri has been keeping an eye on this Tau Rathebe. We've found out he was deported from Johannesburg. Somehow slipped into this farm. And now he's been having secret meetings with three or four of our Kaffirs at a time, to teach them what to do — like today.'

'So! *Hemel!*'

'So you see, Ma, Papa was wrong. I'm going to keep a sharp eye on the black swine. But first thing, I'm ready now to drive Rathebe away; out with him tomorrow.'

At noon the master of Doornvlei made his double decision known: that Tau Rathebe was to leave the farm the following morning, and that Mfukeri had been warned and would be given another chance — the last.

This caused a stir among the labourers, but Tau Rathebe asked them to keep calm.

They wanted to leave with him.

'No. The police will take you as soon as you leave here. You can't go from one farm to another without a trek-pass,' he reminded them.

He left Doornvlei . . .

Sarel Britz felt confused. He kept repeating to himself what he had said to his mother earlier. These are no children, no children . . . they are men . . . I'm dealing with the minds of men . . . My father was

wrong . . . All my boyhood he led me to believe that
black people were children . . . *O Hemel*, they aren't
. . . !

He had begun to see the weakness of his father's
theory during his university years, but it was the
incident with Rathebe that had stamped that
weakness on his mind.

Harvest time came, and Doornvlei became a little
world of intense life and work. The maize triangle of
South Africa was buzzing with talk of a surplus crop
and the threat of low prices.

'A big crop again, Mfukeri, what do you say?' said
Britz.

'Yes, baas,' he grinned consent, 'little bit better
than last year.'

'You know you're a good worker and foreman,
Mfukeri. Without you I don't know how I'd run this
farm.'

'Yes, baas. If baas is happy I'm happy.'

'Since Rathebe left there's peace here, not so?'

'Yes, baas, he makes too much trouble. Long time
I tell baas he always meet the men by the valley.
They talk a long time there. Sometime one man tell
me they want more money and food. I'm happy for
you baas. The old baas he say I must help you all the
time because I work for him fifteen years. I want him
to rest in peace in his grave.'

Britz nodded several times.

The Rhodesian foreman worked as hard as ever to
retain the master's praise. He did not spare himself;
and the other workers had to keep up with his almost
inhuman pace.

'Hey you!' Mfukeri shouted often. 'You there,
you're not working fast enough.' He drove them on,
and some worked in panic, breaking off mealie cobs

and throwing them with the dexterity of a juggler into sacks hanging from the shoulder. Mfukeri did not beat the workers any more. On this Sarel Britz had put his foot down. 'Beat your workers and you lose them,' his father had often said. But every servant felt the foreman's presence and became jittery. And the army of black sweating labourers spread out among the mealie stalks after the systematic fashion of a battle strategy.

Sometimes they sang their songs of grief and hope while reaping in the autumn sun. Sometimes they were too tired even to sing of grief; they just went on working and sweating. There was always a Sunday afternoon to look forward to, when they would go to the village for a drink and song and dance and lovemaking.

Sarel Britz became sterner and more exacting. And his moods and attitude were always reflected in his trusty Mfukeri. Britz kept reminding his tenants that he was just; he favoured no one above the others; he repeated it often to Mfukeri and to his mother. He leaned more and more on his foreman, who realized it and made the most of it.

At university the students had had endless talks about the blacks. Britz had discussed with them his father's theory about allowing the black man a few rungs to climb up at a time — because he was still a child. Most of his colleagues had laughed at this. Gradually he accepted their line of thinking: the white man must be vigilant.

Often when he did his accounts and books, Sarel Britz would stop in the middle of his work, thinking and wondering what he would do if he lost much of his labour, like the other farmers. What if the towns continued to attract the black labourer by offering

him jobs once preserved for the white man? Would
the black workers continue to flow into the towns, or
would the law come to the farmer's rescue by
stopping the influx?

Sarel Britz lived with this fear. At the same time,
he thought, it would break him if he paid his workers
more than forty shillings a month in order to keep
them. A mighty heap of troubles rose before his eyes,
and he could almost hear the shouts and yells of
labour tenants from all the farms rising against their
masters . . .

The threat became more and more real to Britz.
But Mfukeri consoled him. Britz had lately been
inviting him to the house quite often for a chat about
doings on the farm. If only that Kaffir didn't know so
much about the farm so that he, Britz, had to depend
on him more than he cared to . . . 'Come to the house
tonight, Mfukeri, and let's talk,' he said one afternoon in late autumn.

'All right, baas.'

Mfukeri went to see his master. He wondered what
the master had to say. He found him reclining
comfortably in his chair. Mfukeri did not dare to take
a chair before he was told to sit down — always on
the same chair.

'Thank you, baas.'

After a moment of silence, 'What do you think of
me, Mfukeri?'

'Why do you ask me, baas?' — after looking about.

'Don't be afraid to say your mind.'

'You're all right, baas.'

'Sure?'

'Yes, baas.' They smoked silently.

'You still like this farm?

'Very much, baas.'

'I'm glad. You're a good foreman — the only man I trust here.'

Mfukeri understood Britz. He wanted to assure his master that he would never desert him, that he was capable of keeping the tenants together. Hadn't he spied cleverly on Tau Rathebe and avoided an up-heaval?

The foreman felt triumphant. He had never in his life dreamt he would work his way into a white man's trust. He had always felt so inferior before a white man that he despised himself. The more he despised himself the sterner and more ruthless he became towards his fellow-workers. At least he could retain a certain amount of self-respect and the feeling that he was a man, now that his master looked so helpless.

As the foreman sat smoking his pipe, he thought: 'How pitiable they look when they're at a black man's mercy . . . I wonder now . . .'

'All right, Mfukeri,' said the master. The Rhodesian rose and stood erect, like a bluegum tree, over the white man; and the white man thought how in-different his servant looked; just like a tree. To assert his authority once more, Britz gave a few orders.

'Attend to that compost manure first thing tomorrow morning. And also to the cleaning up of the chicken hospital; see to that fanbelt in the threshing machine.'

'Yes, baas, goodnight.'

He was moving towards the door when Britz said, 'Before I forget, be careful about Donker mixing with the cows. It wasn't your fault, of course, but you'll take care, won't you?'

'Yes.' He knew his master regarded his bull Donker as inferior stock, and felt hurt.

It was a bewildered Britz the foreman left behind.

The farmer thought how overwhelming his servant was when he stood before him. Something in him quaked. He was sensitive enough to catch the tone of the last 'baas' when Mfukeri left: it was such an indifferent echo of what 'baas' sounded like years before.

Mfukeri kept a bull with a squatter family on a farm adjoining Doornvlei. Labour tenants were not allowed to keep livestock on the farm on which they themselves worked, because they were paid and received food rations. Mfukeri's friend agreed to keep Donker, the bull, for him. It was a good bull, though scrub.

Two days later Sarel Britz was roused from his lunch hour sleep by a noise outside. He ran out and saw workers hurrying towards a common point. In a few moments he found himself standing near Mfukeri and a group of workers. In front of the barn Britz's pedigree stallion, Kasper, was kicking out at Donker, Mfukeri's bull. Donker had the horse against the barn wall, and was roaring and pawing the earth.

Kasper kicked, a quick barrage of hoofs landing square on the bull's forehead. But the stocky Donker kept coming in and slashing out with his short horns. Normally, there would be ecstatic shouting from the workers. They stood in silence weaving and ducking to follow the movements of the fighters. They couldn't express their attitude towards either side, because they hated both Britz and Mfukeri; and yet the foreman was one of them.

The stallion tried to turn round, which was almost fatal, for Donker charged and unleashed more furious lunging attacks. Master and foreman watched, each feeling that he was entangled in this strife between their animals, more so than they dared to show outwardly. Sarel Britz bit his lower lip as he watched the rage of the bull. He seemed to see scalding fury in the very slime that came from the mouth of the bull to mix with the earth.

He didn't like the slime mixing with the sand: it looked as if Donker were invoking a mystic power in the earth to keep his forehoofs from slipping. Once the hoofs were planted in the ground the bull found an opening and gored Kasper in the stomach, ripping the skin with an upward motion of the horn.

Sarel Britz gave a shout, and walked away hurriedly.

When Mfukeri saw Kasper tottering, and his beloved bull drawing back, an overwhelming feeling of victory shot through every nerve in him. What he had been suppressing all through the fight came out in a gasp and, with tears in his eyes, he shouted: 'Donker! Donker!'

There was a murmur among some of the onlookers who said what a pity it was the horse's hoofs weren't shod; otherwise the ending would have been different.

Kasper was giving his last dying kicks when Britz came back with a rifle in his hand. His face was set. The workers stood aside. Two shots from the rifle finished off the stallion.

'Here, destroy the bull!' he ordered Mfukeri, handing him the gun. The foreman hesitated. 'I said shoot that bull!'

'Why do you want me to shoot my bull, baas?'

'If you don't want to do it, then you must leave this farm, at once!'

Mfukeri did not answer. They both knew the moment had come. He stood still and looked at Britz. Then he walked off, and coaxed his bull out of the premises.

'I gave him a choice,' Sarel said to his mother, telling her the whole story.

'You shouldn't have, Sarel. He has worked for us these fifteen years.'

Sarel knew he had been right. As he looked out of the window to the empty paddock, he was stricken with grief. And then he was glad. He had got rid of yet another threat to his authority.

But the fear remained.

Down the Quiet Street

Nadia Street was reputed to be the quietest street in Newclare. Not that it is any different from other streets. It has its own dirty water, its own flies, its own horse manure, its own pot-bellied children with traces of urine down the legs. The hawker's trolley still slogs along in Nadia Street, and the cloppity-clop from the hoofs of the over-fed mare is still part of the street.

Its rows of houses are no different, either. The roofs slant forward as if they were waiting for the next gale to rock them out of their complacency and complete the work it has already started. Braziers still line the rocky pavement, their columns of smoke curling up and settling on everything around. And stray chickens can be seen pecking at the children's stools with mute relish. Nadia Street has its lean barking mongrels and its share of police beer raids.

Yet the street still clung to the reputation of being the quietest. Things always went on in the *next* street.

Then something happened. When it did, some of

the residents shook their heads dolefully and looked at one another as if they sensed a 100 years' plague round the corner.

Old Lebona down the street laughed and laughed until people feared that his chronic bronchitis was going to strangle him. 'Look at it down the street or up the street,' he said, 'it's the same. People will always do the unexpected. Is it any wonder God's curse remains on the black men?' Then he laughed again.

'You'll see,' said Keledi, rubbing her breast with her forearm to ease the itching caused by the milk. She always said that, to arouse her listeners' curiosity. But she hardly ever showed them what they would see.

Manyeu, the widow, said to her audience: 'It reminds me of what happened once at Winburg, the Boer town down in the Free State.' She looked wistfully ahead of her. The other women looked at her and the new belly that pushed out from under the clean floral apron.

'I remember clearly because I was pregnant, expecting — who was it now? Yes, I was expecting Lusi, my fourth. The one you sent to the butcher yesterday, Kotu.'

Some people said that it happened when Constable Tefo first came to patrol Nadia Street on Sunday afternoons. But others said the 'Russians' — that clan of violent Basotho men — were threatening war. Of course, after it had happened Nadia Street went back to what its residents insisted on calling a quiet life.

If Constable Tefo ever thought that he could remain untouched by Nadia Street gossip, he was jolly well mistaken. The fact that he found it necessary to make up his mind about it indicated that he feared the possibility of being entangled in the people's private lives.

He was tall and rather good-looking. There was nothing officious about him, nothing police-looking except for the uniform. He was in many ways one of the rarest of the collection from the glass cage at Headquarters. His bosses suspected him. He looked to them too human to be a good protector of the law. Yes, that's all he was to the people, that's what his bosses had hired him for.

The news spread that Tefo was in love. 'I've seen the woman come here at the end of every month. He always kisses her. The other day I thought he was kissing her too long.' That was Manyeu's verdict.

It did not seem to occur to anyone that the woman who was seen kissing Tefo might be his wife. Perhaps it was just as well, because it so happened that he did not have a wife. At 40 he was still unmarried.

Manyeu was struck almost silly when Constable Tefo entered her house to buy 'maheu' (sour mealie-meal drink).

'You'll see,' said Keledi, who rubbed her breast up and down to relieve the burning itch of the milk.

Still Tefo remained at his post, almost like a mountain: at once defiant, reassuring, and menacing. He would not allow himself to be ruffled by the subtle suggestions he heard, the meaningful twitch of the face he saw, the burning gaze he felt behind him as he moved about on his beat.

One day Keledi passed him with a can of beer, holding it behind her apron. She chatted with him for a while and they both laughed. It was like that often; mice playing hide and seek in the mane of the lion.

'How's business?' Tefo asked Sung Li's wife one Sunday on the stoep of their shop.

'Velly bad.'

'Why?'

'Times is bad.'

'Hm.'

'Velly beezee, you?'

'Yes, no rest, till we get over there, at Croesus Cemetery.'

She laughed, thinking it very funny that a policeman should think of death. She told him so.

'How's China?'

'I'm not from China, he, he, he. I'm born here, he, he, he. Funnee!' And she showed rusty rotten teeth when she laughed, the top front teeth overtaking the receding lower row, not co-operating in the least to present a good-looking jaw.

Tefo laughed loud to think that he had always thought of the Sung Lis as people from China, which, from what he had been told in his childhood, conjured up weird pictures of man-eating people.

When he laughed, Constable Tefo's stomach moved up and down while he held his belt in front and his shoulders fluttered about like the wings of a bird that is not meant to fly long distances.

When her husband within called her, Madam Sung Li turned to go. Tefo watched her shuffling her small feet, slippers almost screaming with the pain of being dragged like that. From behind, the edge of the dress clung alternatively to the woollen black stockings she had on. The bundle of hair at the back of her head looked as if all the woman's fibre were knotted up in it, and that if it were undone, Madam Sung Li might fall to pieces. Her body bent forward like a tree in the wind. Tefo observed to himself that there was no wind.

One Sunday afternoon Tefo entered Sung Li's shop to buy a bottle of lemonade. The heat was intense. The roofs of the houses seemed to strain under the merciless pounding of the sun. All available windows and doors were ajar and, owing to the general lack of verandahs and the total absence of trees, the residents puffed and sighed and groaned and stripped off some of their garments.

Madam Sung Li leaned over the counter, her elbows planted on the top surface, her arms folded. She might have been the statue of some Oriental god in that position but for a lazy afternoon fly that tried to settle on her face. She had to throw her head about to keep the pestilent insect away.

Constable Tefo breathed hard after every gulp as he stood looking out through the shop window, facing Nadia Street.

One thing he had got used to was the countless funeral processions that trailed on week after week. They had to pass Newclare on the way to the cemetery. Short ones, long ones, hired double deckers, cars, lorries; poor insignificant ones, rich snobbish ones. All black and inevitable.

The processions usually took the street next to Nadia. But so many people were dying that some units were beginning to spill over into Nadia.

Tefo went out to the stoep to have a little diversion; anything to get his mind off the heat. He was looking at one short procession as it turned into Nadia when a thought crossed his mind, like the shadow of a cloud that passes under the sun.

Seleke's cousin came staggering onto the stoep. His clothes looked as if he had once crossed many rivers and drained at least one. He was always referred to as Seleke's cousin, and nobody ever cared to know his name.

Seleke lived in the next street. She was the tough sort with a lashing tongue. But even she could not whip her cousin out of his perennial stupor.

Keledi's comment was: 'You'll see, one day he'll hunt mice for food. The cats won't like it.' And she rubbed her breast. But Seleke's cousin absorbed it all without the twinge of a hair.

'Ho, chief!' Seleke's cousin hailed the constable, wobbling about like a puppet on the stage. 'Watching the coffins, eh? Too many people dying, eh? Yes, too many. Poor devils.'

Tefo nodded. A lorry drove up the street, and pulled up on the side, almost opposite the China- man's shop.

'Dead men don't shout,' said Seleke's cousin.

'You're drunk. Why don't you go home and sleep?'

'Me drunk? Yes, yes, I'm drunk. But don't you talk to me like these pigheaded people around here. Their pink tongues wag too much. Why don't they leave me alone? There's no-one in this bloody location who can read English like I do.'

'I'm sure there isn't.' Tefo smiled tolerantly.

'I like you, chief. You're going to be a great man one of these days. Now, you're looking at these people going to bury their dead. One of these days those coffins will tell their story. I don't know why they can't leave me alone. Why can't they let me be, the lousy lot?'

A small funeral party turned into Nadia Street on a horse-drawn trolley cart. There were three women and four men on the cart, excluding the driver. A man who looked like their religious leader sang lustily, his voice quivering above the others.

The leader had on a frayed, fading, purple surplice and an off-white cassock. He looked rather too young for such a mighty responsibility as trying to direct departed souls to heaven, Tefo thought. The constable also thought how many young men were being fired with religious feelings these days . . . The trolley stopped in front of a house almost opposite Sung Li's. Tefo looked on. The group alighted and the four men lifted the coffin down.

Tefo noticed that the leader was trembling. By some miracle his hymn book stayed in the trembling hand. He wiped his forehead so many times that the constable thought the leader had a fever and could not lift the coffin further. They obviously wanted to enter the yard just behind them. He went to the spot and offered to help.

The leader's eyes were wide and they reflected a host of emotions Tefo could not understand. And then he made a surprising gesture to stop Tefo from touching the coffin. In a second he nodded his head several times, muttering something that made Tefo understand that his help would be appreciated. Whereupon the constable picked up the handle on his side, and the quartet took the corpse into the house. Soon Tefo was back on the Chinaman's stoep.

It must have been about fifteen minutes later when he heard voices bursting out in song as the party came out of the house with the coffin. Again Tefo noticed the leader was sweating and trembling. The coffin was put on the ground outside the gate. The others in the party continued to sing lustily, the men's voices beating down the courageous sopranos.

Tefo sensed that they wanted to hoist it onto the lorry. Something told him he should not go and help. One of these religious sects with queer rules, he thought.

At the gate the leader of the funeral party bent forward and, with a jerky movement, he caught hold of the handle and tilted the coffin, shouting to the other men at the same time to hold the handles on their side. Tefo turned sharply to look.

A strange sound came from the box. To break the downward tilt the other men had jerked the coffin up. But a cracking sound came from the bottom; a sound of cracking wood. They were going to hoist the coffin higher, when it happened.

A miniature avalanche of bottles came down to the ground. A man jumped into the lorry, reversed it a little and drove off. The trolley cart ground its way down Nadia Street. Tefo's eyes swallowed the whole scene. He descended from the stoep as if in a trance, and walked slowly to the spot. It was a scene of liquor bottles tumbling and tinkling and bumping into one another, some breaking, and others rolling down the street in a playful manner, like children who have been let out of the classroom at playtime. There was hissing and shouting among the funeral party.

'You frightened goat!'

'Messing up the whole business!'

'I knew this would happen!'

'You'll pay for this!'

'You should have stayed home, you clumsy pumpkin!'

'We're ruined this time!'

They had all disappeared by the time it had registered on Tefo's mind that an arrest must be made. More than that: a wild mob of people was scrambling for the bottles. In a moment they also had disappeared with the bottles, the corpus delicti! A number of people gathered round the policeman.

The lousy crowd, he thought, glad that a police-man had failed to arrest! They nudged one another, and others indulged in mock pity. Manyeu came forward. 'I want the box for fire, sir constable.' He indicated impatiently with the hand that she might have it. It did not escape Keledi's attention, and she said to her neighbour, rubbing her breast that was full of milk: 'You'll see. Wait.'

'Ho, chief! Trouble here?' Seleke's cousin elbowed his way to the centre of the crowd. He had been told what had happened.

'Funerals, funerals, funerals is my backside! Too bad I'm late for the party! Hard luck to you, chief. Now listen, I trust these corpses like the lice on my shirt. But you're going to be a great man one day. Trust my word for that. I bet the lice on my body.'

Later that afternoon Constable Tefo sat in Manyeu's room, drinking 'maheu'. Keledi, rubbing her breast, was sitting on the floor with two other women. Manyeu sat on a low bench, her new belly pushing out under her floral apron like a promising melon.

Somewhat detached from the women's continuous babble, Tefo was thinking about funerals and corpses and bottles of liquor. He wondered about funeral processions in general. He remembered what Seleke's cousin had said the other day on the Chinaman's stoep. Was it an unwitting remark? Just then another procession passed down the street. Tefo stood up abruptly and went to stand at the door. If only the gods could tell him what was in that brown glossy coffin, he thought. He went back to his bench, a figure of despair.

Keledi's prophetic 'You'll see' took on a serious meaning when Tefo one day married Manyeu after her sixth had arrived. Nadia Street gasped. But then recovered quickly from the surprise, considering the reputation it had of being the quietest street in Newclare.

It added to Keledi's social stature to be able to say after the event: 'You see!' while she vigorously rubbed her breasts that itched from the milk.

The Coffee–Cart Girl

The crowd moved like one mighty being, and swayed and swung like the sea. In front of them was Metropolitan Steel Windows Ltd. All eyes were fixed on it. Its workers did not hear one another: perhaps they didn't need to, each one interested as he was in what he was saying — and that with his blood. All he knew was that he was on strike: for what? If you asked him he would just spit and say: 'Do you think we've come to play?'

Grimy, oily, greasy, sweating black bodies squeezed and chafed and grated. Pickets were at work; the law was brandishing batons; cars were hooting a crazy medley.

'Stand back, you monkeys!' cried a black man pinned against a pillar. 'Hey, you black son of a black hen!'

The coffee-cart girl was absorbed in the very idea of the Metropolitan Steel Windows strike, just as she was in the flood of people who came to buy her coffee and pancakes: she wasn't aware of the swelling crowd and its stray atoms which were being flung out of it towards her cart until she heard an ear-splitting crash behind her. One of the row of coffee-carts had tipped over and a knot of men fallen on it. She climbed down from her cart, looking like a bird frightened out of its nest.

A woman screamed. Another crash. The man who had been pinned against the pillar had freed himself and he found himself standing beside the girl. He sensed her predicament. Almost rudely he pushed her into the street, took the cart by the stump of a shaft and wheeled it across the street, shouting generally, 'Give way, you black monkeys.' Just then a cart behind him went down and caved in like matchwood.

'Oh, thank you so much, mister!'

'Ought to be more careful, my sister.'

'How can I thank you! Here, take coffee and a pancake.'

'Thank you, my sister.'

'Look, they're moving forward, maybe to break into the factory!' When next she looked back he was gone. And she hadn't even asked him his name: how unfriendly of her, she thought . . .

Later that winter morning the street was cleared of most people. The workers had gone away. There had been no satisfactory agreement. Strikes were unlawful for black people anyhow.

'Come back to work, or you are signed off, or go to gaol,' had come the stock executive order. More than half had been signed off.

It was comparatively quiet now in this squalid West End sector of the city. Men and women continued their daily round. A dreary smoky mist lingered in suspension, or clung to the walls; black sooty chimneys shot up malignantly; there was a strong smell of bacon; the fruit and vegetable shops resumed trade with a tremulous expectancy; old men stood Buddha-like at the entrances with folded arms and a vague grimace on their faces, seeming to sneer at the world in general and their contemptible mercantile circle in particular; and the good earth is generous enough to contain all the human sputum these good suffering folk shoot out of their mouths at the slightest provocation. A car might tear down the cross-street and set up a squall and sweep dry horse manure so that it circled in the air in a momentary spree, increasing the spitting gusto . . .

'Hello.'

'Hello, want coffee?'

'Yes, and two hot buns.'

She hardly looked at him as she served him. For a brief spell her eyes fell on the customer. Slowly she gathered up the scattered bits of memory and unconsciously the picture was framed. She looked at him and found him scanning her.

'Oh!' She gave a gasp and her hand went to her mouth. 'You're the good uncle who saved my cart!'

'Don't uncle me, please. My name is Ruben Lemeko. The boys at the factory call me China. Yours?'

'Zodwa.'

His eyes travelled from her small tender fingers as she washed a few things, to her man's jersey which was a faded green and too big for her, her thin frock, and then to her peach-coloured face, not well fed, but well framed and compelling under a soiled black beret. As he ate hungrily she shot a side-glance at him occasionally. There was something sly in those soft, moist, slit eyes, but the modest stoop at the shoulders gave him a benign appearance; otherwise he would

have looked twisted and rather fiendish. There was
something she felt in his presence: a repelling
admiration. She felt he was the kind of man who
could be quite attractive so long as he remained more
than a touch away from the contemplator; just like
those wax figures she once saw in the chamber of
horrors.

'Signed off at the Metropolitan?'

'Hm.' His head drooped and she could read
dejection in the oily top of his cap. 'Just from the
insurance fund office.' She pitied him inwardly, a sort
of pity she had never before experienced for a strange
man.

'What to do now?'

'Like most of us,' looking up straight into her eyes,
'beat the road early mornings just when the boss's
breakfast is settling nicely in the stomach. No work,
no government papers, no papers, no work, then out
of town.'

'It's hard for everybody, I guess.'

'Ja.'

'I know. When you feel hungry and don't have
money, come past here and I'll give you coffee and
pancake.'

'Thanks, er — let me call you Pinkie, shall I?'

'Hm,' she nodded automatically.

He shook her hand. 'Grow as big as an elephant for
your goodness, as we say in our idiom.' He shuffled
off. For a long time, until he disappeared, she didn't
take her eyes off the stooping figure, which she felt
might set any place on fire. Strange man, Pinkie
thought idly as she washed up.

China often paused at Pinkie's coffee-cart. But he
wouldn't let her give him coffee and pancakes for

nothing.

'I'm no poorer than you,' he said. 'When I'm really in the drain pipes you may come to my help.'

As she got used to him and the idea of a tender playfellow who is capable of scratching blood out of you, she felt heartily sorry for him; and he detected it, and resented it and felt sorry for her in turn.

'Right, Pinkie, I'll take it today.'

'You'll starve to death in this cruel city.'

'And then? Lots of them starve; think of this mighty city, Pinkie. What are we, you and me? If we starved and got sick and died, who'd miss you and me?'

Days when China didn't come, she missed him. And then she was afraid of something; something mysterious that crawls into human relations, and before we know it it's there; and because it is frightening it does not know how to announce itself without causing panic and possibly breaking down bonds of companionship. In his presence she tried to take refuge in an artless sisterly pity for him. And although he resented it, he carried on a dumb show. Within, heaven and earth thundered and rocked, striving to meet; sunshine and rain mingled; milk and gall pretended friendship; fire and water went hand in hand; tears and laughter hugged each other in a fit of hysterics; the screeching of the hang-bird started off with the descant of a dove's cooing; devils waved torches before a chorus of angels. Pinkie and China panicked at the thought of a love affair and remained dumb.

'Pinkie, I've got a job at last!'

'I'm happy for you, China!'

'You'll get a present, first money I get. Ach, but I shouldn't have told you. I wanted to surprise you.'

He was genuinely sorry.

'Don't worry, China, I'll just pretend I'm surprised really, you'll see.' They laughed.

Friday came.

'Come, Pinkie, let's go.'

'Where to?'

'I'll show you.' He led her to the cheapjack down the street.

'Mister, I want her to choose anything she wants.'

The cheapjack immediately sprang up and in voluble cataracts began to heap praises upon his articles.

'All right, mister, let me choose.' Pinkie picked up one article after another, inspected it, and at last she selected a beautiful long bodkin, a brooch, and a pair of bangles. Naidoo, the cheapjack, went off into rhapsodies again on Pinkie's looks when China put the things on her himself, pinning the bodkin on her beret. He bought himself a knife, dangling from a fashionable chain. They went back to the coffee-cart.

From that day onwards, Naidoo became a frequent customer at Pinkie's coffee-cart. He often praised her cakes and coffee. Twice at lunch-time China found him relating some anecdotes which sent Pinkie off into peals of laughter.

'Where you work, my prend?' asked Naidoo one day. He ran his words together and he would say 'pore-pipty' for 'four fifty', 'pier foms' for 'five forms', 'werry wital' for 'very vital'.

'Shoe factory, Main Street.'

'Good pay?'

'Where do you find such a thing in this city?'

'Quite right, my prend. Look at me: I was wanted to be a grocer, and now I'm a cheapjack.'

'I'm hungry today, Pinkie,' China said one day. He

was clearly elated over something.

'It's so beautiful to see you happy, China, what's the news?'

'Nothing. Hasn't a man the right to be jolly sometimes?'

'Of course. Just wondered if anything special happened.'

He looked at her almost transparent pink fingers as she washed the coffee things.

'Hey, you've a lovely ring on your finger, where's the mine?'

Pinkie laughed as she looked at the glass-studded ring, fingered it and wiped it.

'From Naidoo.'

'What?'

'It's nothing, China, Naidoo didn't have any money for food, so he offered me this for three days' coffee and cakes.' She spoke as if she didn't believe her own story. She sensed a gathering storm.

'You lie!'

'Honestly China, now what would I be lying for?'

So! he thought, she couldn't even lie to keep their friendship: how distant she sounded. His fury mounted.

'Yes, you lie! Now listen Pinkie, you're in love with that cheapjack. Every time I found him here he's been damn happy with you, grinning and making eyes at you. Yes, I've watched him every moment.'

He approached the step leading into the cart.

'Do you see me? I've loved you since I first saw you, the day of the strike.' He was going to say more, but something rose inside him and choked him. He couldn't utter a word more. He walked slowly, a knife drawn out, with a menacing blade pointed towards her throat. Pinkie retreated deeper into her cart, too frightened to plead her case.

At that very moment she realised fully the ghastliness of a man's jealousy, which gleamed and glanced on the blade and seemed to have raised a film which steadied the slit eyes. Against the back wall she managed to speak.

'All right, China, maybe you've done this many times before. Go ahead and kill me; I won't cry for help, do what you like with me.'

She panted like a timid little mouse cornered by a cat. He couldn't finish the job he had set out to do. Why? He had sent two men packing with a knife before. They had tried to fight, but this creature wasn't resisting at all. Why, why, why? He felt the heat pounding in his temples; the knife dropped, and he sank onto a stool and rested his head on the wall, his hands trembling.

After a moment he stood up, looking away from Pinkie. 'I'm sorry, Pinkie, I pray you never in your life to think about this day.'

She looked at him, mystified.

'Say you forgive me.' She nodded twice.

Then she packed up for the day, much earlier than usual.

The following day China did not visit Pinkie; nor the next. He could not decide to go there. Things were all in a barbed wire tangle in his mind. But see her he must, he thought. He would just go and hug her; say nothing but just press her to himself because he felt too mean even to tell her not to be afraid of him any more.

The third day the law came. It marched up the street in goose-step fashion. The steel on its heels clanged on the pavement with an ominous echo. It gave commands and everything came to an end at once. Black man's coffee-cart was not to operate any more in the city. ' . . . Makes the city look ugly,' the city fathers said.

For several days China, unaware of what had happened, called on Pinkie, but always found the coffee-carts empty and deserted. At last he learned everything from Naidoo, the cheapjack.

He stepped into her coffee-cart and sat on the stool.

He looked into the cheerless pall of smoke. Outside life went on as if there had never been a Pinkie who sold coffee and pancakes.

Dare he hope that she would come back, just to meet him? Or was it going to turn out to have been a dream? He wondered.

We'll meet in town, some day, China thought. I'll tell her all about myself, all about my wicked past; she'll get used to me, not be afraid of me any more . . .

And still he sat in the coffee-cart which was once Pinkie's, all through the lunch-hour . . .

The Living and the Dead

Lebona felt the letter burning in his pocket. Since he had picked it up along the railway it had nagged at him no end.

He would read it during his lunch, he thought. Meantime he must continue with his work, which was to pick up rubbish that people continuously threw on the platform and on the railway tracks. Lebona used a piece of wire with a ball of tar stuck on at the end. One didn't need to bend. One only pressed the ball of tar on a piece of paper or any other rubbish, detached it and threw it into a bag hanging from the shoulder.

A number of things crossed Lebona's mind: the man who had died the previous afternoon. Died, just like that. How could a man just die like that — like a rat or a mere dog?

The workers' rush was over. Only a few women sat on the benches on the platform. One was following his movements with her eyes. She sat there, so fat, he observed, looking at him. Just like a woman. She just sat and looked at you for no reason; probably because of an idle mind; maybe she was thinking about everything. Still he knew if he were a fly she might look at him all day. But no, not the letter. She mustn't be thinking about it. The letter in his pocket. It wasn't hers — no, it couldn't be; he had picked it up lower down the line; she could say what she liked, but it wasn't her letter.

That man: who would have thought a man could die just as if death were in one's pocket or throat all the time?

Stoffel Visser was angry; angry because he felt foolish. Everything had gone wrong. And right through his university career Stoffel Visser had been taught that things must go right to the last detail.

'Calm yourself, Stoffel.'

'Such mistakes shouldn't ever occur.'

'Don't preach, for God's sake!'

Doppie Fourie helped himself to more whisky.

'It's all Jackson's fault,' Stoffel said. 'He goes out yesterday and instead of being here in the evening to prepare supper he doesn't come. This morning he's still not here, still not here, and I can't get my bloody breakfast in time because I've got to do it myself, and you know I *must* have a good breakfast every day. Worse, my clock is out of order, buggered up man, and the bloody Jackson's not here to wake me up. So I oversleep — that's what happens — and after last night's *braaivleis,* you know. It's five o'clock on a Friday morning, and the bastard hasn't turned up yet. How could I be in time to give Rens the document before the Cape Town train left this morning?'

'Now I think of it, Stoffel,' said Fourie, 'I can't help thinking how serious the whole thing is. Now the Minister can't have the report to think about it before the session begins. What do we do next?'

'There'll still be time enough to post it by express mail.'

Doppie Fourie looked grave.

'You don't have to look as if the sky was about to fall,' he said, rather to himself than to his friend. 'Have another whisky.'

Stoffel poured one for himself and his friend. 'What a good piece of work we did, Doppie!'

'Bloody good. Did you see this?' Fourie held out a newspaper, pointing his trembling finger at a report. The item said that Africans had held a 'roaring party' in a suburban house while the white family were out. There had been feasting and music and dancing.

'See, you see now,' said Stoffel, unable to contain his emotion. 'Just what I told these fellows on the commission. Some of them are so wooden-headed they won't understand simple things like kaffirs swarming over our suburbs, living there, gambling there, breeding there, drinking there and sleeping there with girls. They won't understand, these stupid fools, until the kaffirs enter their houses and boss them about and sleep with white girls. What's to happen to white civilisation?'

'Don't make another speech, Stoffel. We've talked about this so long in the commission I'm simply choking with it.'

'Look here, Doppie Fourie, *ou kêrel,* you deceive yourself to think I want to hear myself talk.'

'I didn't mean that, Stoffel. But of course you have always been very clever. I envy you your brains. You always have a ready answer to a problem. Anyhow I don't promise to be an obedient listener tonight. I just want to drink.'

'C'mon, *ou kêrel,* you know you want to listen. If I feel pressed to speak you must listen, like it or not.'

Doppie looked up at Stoffel, this frail-looking man with an artist's face and an intellect that seldom rose to the surface. None of our Rugby-playing types with their bravado, Doppie thought. Often he hated himself for feeling so inferior. And all through his friend's miniature oration Doppie's face showed a deep hurt.

'Let me tell you this, *rooinekke,*' Stoffel said, 'you know I'd rather be touring the whole world and meeting people and cultures and perhaps be learning some art myself — I know you don't believe a thing I'm saying — instead of rotting in this hole and tolerating numskulls I'm compelled to work with on committees. Doppie, there must be hundreds of our people who'd rather be doing something else they love best. But we're all tied to some bucking bronco and we must like it while we're still here and work ourselves up into a national attitude. And we've to keep talking, man. We haven't much time to waste looking at both sides of the question like these stupids, *ou kêrel.* That's why it doesn't pay any more to pretend we're being just and fair to the kaffir by controlling him. No use even trying to tell him he's going to like living in enclosures.

'Isn't it because we know what the kaffir wants that we must call a halt to his ambitious wants? The danger, as I see it, *ou kêrel,* isn't merely in the kaffir's increasing anger and desperation. It also lies in our tendency as whites to believe that what we tell him is the truth. And this might drive us to sleep one day — a fatal day, I tell you. It's necessary to keep talking, Doppie, so as to keep jolting the whites into a sharp awareness. It's dangerously easy for the public to forget and go to sleep.'

Doppie clapped his hands in applause, half-dazed, half-mocking, half-admiring. At such times he never

knew what word could sum up Stoffel Visser. A
genius? — yes, he must be. And then Stoffel would
say things he had so often heard from others. Ag, I
knew it — just like all of us — ordinarily stubborn
behind those deep-set eyes. And thinking so gave
Doppie a measure of comfort. He distrusted complex
human beings because they evaded labels. Life would
be so much nicer if one could just take a label out of
the pocket and tack it on the lapel of a man's coat.
Like the one a lady pins on you to show that you've
dropped a coin into her collecting box. As a badge of
charity.

'We can't talk too much, *ou kêrel*. We haven't said
the last word in that report on kaffir servants in the
suburbs.'

Day and night for three months Stoffel Visser had
worked hard for the commission he was secretary of
— the Social Affairs Commission of his Christian
Protestant Party. The report of the commission was
to have been handed to Tollen Rens, their representative in Parliament, who, in turn, had to discuss it with
a member of the Cabinet. A rigorous remedy was
necessary, it was suggested, for what Stoffel had
continually impressed on the minds of his cronies as
'an ugly situation'. He could have chopped his own
head off for failing to keep his appointment with
Tollen Rens. And all through Jackson's not coming to
wake him up and give him the breakfast he was used
to enjoying with an unflagging appetite.

'Right, Stoffel, see you tomorrow at the office.'
Doppie Fourie was leaving. Quite drunk. He rocked
on his heel a bit as he made for the door, a vacant
smile playing on his lips.

Although the two men had been friends for a long
time, Doppie Fourie could never stop himself feeling

humiliated after a serious talk with Stoffel. Visser always overwhelmed him, beat him down and trampled on him with his superior intellect. The more he drank in order to blunt the edge of the pain Stoffel unwittingly caused him, the deeper was the hurt Doppie felt whenever they had been talking shop. Still, if Fourie never had the strength of mind to wrench himself from Stoffel's grip, his friend did all he could to preserve their companionship, if only as an exhaust-pipe for his mental energy.

Stoffel's mind slowly came back to his rooms — to Jackson in particular. He liked Jackson, his cook, who had served him with the devotion of a trained animal and ministered to all his bachelor whims and eating habits for four years. As he lived in a flat, it was not necessary for Jackson to do the cleaning. This was the work of the cleaner hired by Stoffel's landlord.

Jackson had taken his usual Thursday off. He had gone to Shanty-Town, where his mother-in-law lived with his two children, in order to fetch them and take them to the zoo. He had promised so many times to take them there. His wife worked in another suburb. She couldn't go with them to the zoo because, she said, she had the children's sewing to finish.

This was the second time that Jackson had not turned up when he was expected after taking a day off. The first time he had returned the following morning, all apologies. Where could the confounded kaffir be, Stoffel wondered. But he was too busy trying to adjust his mood to the new situation to think of the different things that might have happened to Jackson.

Stoffel's mind turned around in circles without ever coming to a fixed point. It was this, that, and then everything. His head was ringing with the voices he had heard so many times at recent meetings. Angry voices of residents who were gradually being incensed by speakers like him, frantic voices that demanded that the number of servants in each household be brought down because it wouldn't do for blacks to run the suburbs from their quarters in European backyards.

But there were also angry voices from other meetings: if you take the servants away, how are they going to travel daily to be at work on time, before we leave for work ourselves? Other voices: who told you there are too many natives in our yards? Then others: we want to keep as many servants as we can afford.

And the voices became angrier and angrier, roaring like a sea in the distance and coming nearer and nearer to shatter his complacency. The voices spoke in different languages, gave different arguments, often using different premises to assert the same principles. They spoke in soft, mild tones and in urgent and hysterical moods.

The mind turned around the basic arguments in a turmoil: you shall not, we will; we can, you can't; they shall not, they shall; why must they? Why mustn't they? Some of these kaffir lovers, of course, hate the thought of having to forego the fat feudal comfort of having cheap labour within easy reach when we remove black servants to their own locations, Stoffel mused.

And amid these voices he saw himself working and sweating to create a theory to defend ready-made attitudes, stock attitudes that various people had each in their own time planted in him: his mother, his father, his brothers, his friends, his schoolmasters, his university professors and all the others who claimed him as their own. He was fully conscious of the whole process in his mind. Things had to be done with conviction or not at all.

Then, even before he knew it, those voices became an echo of other voices coming down through the centuries: the echo of gun-fire, cannon, wagon-wheels as they ground away over stone and sand; the echo of hate and vengeance. All he felt was something in his blood which groped back through the corridors of history to pick up some of the broken threads that linked his life with a terrible past. He surrendered himself to it all, to this violent desire to remain part of a brutal historic past, lest he should be crushed by the brutal necessities of the present, and be forced to lose his identity: Almighty God, no, no! Unconsciously he was trying to pile on layers of crocodile hide over his flesh to protect himself against thoughts or feelings that might some day in the vague future threaten to hurt.

When he woke from a stupor, Stoffel Visser remembered Jackson's wife over at Greenside. He had not asked her if she knew where his servant was. He jumped up and dialled on his telephone. He called Virginia's employer and asked him. No, Virginia didn't know where her husband was. As far as she knew her husband had told her the previous Sunday that he was going to take the children to the zoo. What could have happened to her husband, she wanted to know. Why hadn't he telephoned the police? Why hadn't he phoned Virginia in the morning? Virginia's master asked him these and several other questions. He got annoyed because he couldn't answer them.

None of the suburban police stations or Marshall

Square Station had Jackson's name in their charge
books. They would let him know 'if anything turned
up'. A young voice from one police station said
perhaps Stoffel's 'kaffir' had gone to sleep with his
'maid' elsewhere and had forgotten to turn up for
work. Or, he suggested, Jackson might be under a
hang-over in the location. 'You know what these
kaffirs are.' And he laughed with a thin sickly voice.
Stoffel banged the receiver down.

There was a light knock at the door of his flat.
When he opened it with anticipation he saw an
African standing erect, hat in hand.

'Yes?'

'Yes, *Baas.*'

'What do you want?'

'I bring you this, *Baas,*' handing a letter to the
white man, while he thought: *just like those white
men who work for the railways . . . it's good I sealed
it . . .*

'Whose is this? It's addressed here, to Jackson!
Where did you find it?'

'I was clean the line, *Baas.* Um pick papers and
rubbish on railway line at Park Stish. Um think of
something as um work. Then I pick up this. I ask *my*-
self, who could have dropped it? But . . . '

'All right, why didn't you take it to your boss?'

'They keep letters there many months, *Baas,* and
no one comes for them.' His tone suggested that
Stoffel should surely know that.

*The cheek he has, finding fault with the way the
white man does things.*

'You lie! You opened it first to see what's inside.
When you found no money you sealed it up and were
afraid your boss would find out you had opened it.
Not true?'

'It's not true, *Baas*, I was going to bring it here whatever happened.'

He fixed his eyes on the letter in Stoffel's hand. 'Truth's God, *Baas*,' Lebona said, happy to be able to lie to someone who had no way of divining the truth, thinking at the same time: *they're not even decent enough to suspect one's telling the truth!*

They always lie to you when you're white, Stoffel thought, *just for cheek.*

The more Lebona thought he was performing a just duty the more annoyed the white man was becoming.

'Where do you live?'

'Kensington, *Baas*. Um go there now. My wife she working there.'

Yet another of them, eh? Going home in a white man's area — we'll put a stop to that yet — and look at the smugness on his mug!

'All right, go.' All the time they were standing at the door, Stoffel thought how the black man smelled of sweat, even though he was standing outside.

Lebona made to go and then remembered something. Even before the white man asked him further he went on to relate it all, taking his time, with his emotions spilling over.

'I feel very sore in my heart, *Baas*. This poor man, he comes out of train. There are only two lines of steps on platform, and I say to *my*-self how can people go up when others are coming down? You know, there are iron gates now, and only one go and come at a time. Now other side there's train to leave for Orlando.'

What the hell have I to do with this? What does he think this is, a complaints office?

'Now, you see, it's like this: a big crowd go up and a big crowd want to rush for their train. Um look and

whistle and says to *my*-self how can people move in
different ways like that? Like a river going against
another!'

One of these kaffirs who think they're smart, eh.

'This man, I've been watching him go up. I see him
pushed down by those on top of steps. rush down
and stamp on him and kick him. He rolls down until
he drops back on platform. Blood comes out mouth
and nose like rain and I say to *my*-self, oho he's dead,
poor man!'

*I wish he didn't keep me standing here listening
to a story about a man I don't even care to know!
. . .*

'The poor man died, just like that, just as if I went
down the stairs now and then you hear um dead.'

I couldn't care less, either . . .

'As um come here by tram I think, perhaps this is
his letter.'

'All right now, I'll see about that.'

Lebona walked off with a steady and cautious but
firm step. Stoffel was greatly relieved.

Immediately he rang the hospital and mortuary,
but there was no trace of Jackson. Should he or
should he not read the letter? It might give him a
clue. But, no, he wasn't a *kaffir!*

Another knock at the door.

Jackson's wife, Virginia, stood just where Lebona
had stood a few minutes before.

'He's not yet here, Master?'

'No.' Impulsively he showed her to a chair in the
kitchen. 'Where else could he have gone?'

'Don't know, Master.' Then she started to cry,
softly. 'Sunday we were together, Master, at my
master's place. We talked about our children and you
know one is seven the other four and few months and

firstborn is just like his father with eyes and nose and they have always been told about the zoo by play-mates so they wanted to go there, so Jackson promised them he would take them to see the animals.' She paused, sobbing quietly, as if she meant that to be the only way she could punctuate her speech.

'And the smaller child loves his father so and he's Jackson's favourite. You know Nkati the elder one was saying to his father the other day the day their grandmother brought them to see us — he says I wish you die, just because his father wouldn't give him more sweets. Lord he's going to be the rebel of the family and he needs a strong man's hand to keep him straight. And now if Jackson is — is — oh Lord God above.'

She sobbed freely now.

'All right. I'll try my best to find him, wherever he may be. You may go now, because it's time for me to lock up.'

'Thank you, Master.' She left.

Stoffel stepped into the street and got into his car to drive five miles to the nearest police station. For the first time in his life he left his flat to look for a black man because he meant much to him — at any rate as a servant.

Virginia's pathetic look; her roundabout un-punctuated manner of saying things; the artless and devoted Virginia; the railway worker and his I-don't-care-whether-you're-listening manner; the picture of two children who might very well be fatherless as he was driving through the suburb; the picture of a dead man rolling down station steps and of Lebona pouring out his heart over a man he didn't know . . . These images turned round and round into a complex knot. He had got into the habit of thinking in terms of irreconcilable contradictions, opposition and categories. Black was black, white was white — that was all that mattered.

So he couldn't at the moment answer the questions that kept bobbing up from somewhere in his soul; sharp little questions coming without ceremony; sharp little questions shooting up, sometimes like meteors, sometimes like darts, sometimes climbing up like a slow winter's sun. He was determined to resist them. He found it so much easier to think out categories and to place people.

His friend at the police station promised to help him.

The letter. Why hadn't he given it to Jackson's wife? After all, she had just as much right to possess it as her husband?

Later he couldn't resist the temptation to open the envelope; after all, it might hold a clue. He carefully broke open the flap. There were charming photographs, one of a man and woman, the other of two children, evidently theirs. They were Jackson's all right.

The letter inside was written to Jackson himself. Stoffel read it. It was from somewhere in Vendaland, from Jackson's father. He was very ill and did not expect to live much longer. Would Jackson come soon because the government people were telling him to get rid of some of his cattle to save the land from washing away, and will Jackson come soon so that he might attend to the matter because he, the old man, was powerless. He had only the strength to tell the government people that it was more land the people wanted and not less stock. He had heard the white man used certain things to stop birth in human beings, and if the white man thought he was going to do the same with his cattle and donkeys — that would be the day a donkey would give birth to a cow. But alas, he said, he had only enough strength to swear by the gods his stock wouldn't be thinned down. Jackson must come soon. He was sending the photographs which he loved very much and would like them to be safe because he might die any moment. He was sending the letter through somebody who was travelling to the gold city.

The ending was:

May the gods bless you my son and my daughter-in-law and my lovely grandsons. I shall die in peace because I have had the heavenly joy of holding my grandsons on my knees.

It was in a very ugly scrawl without any punctuation marks. With somewhat unsteady hands Stoffel put the things back in the envelope.

Monday lunch-time Stoffel Visser motored to his flat, just to check up. He found Jackson in his room lying on his bed. His servant's face was all swollen up with clean bandages covering the whole head and cheeks. His eyes sparkled from the surrounding puffed flesh.

'Jackson!'

His servant looked up at him.

'What happened?'

'The police.'

'Where?'

'Victoria Police Station.'

'Why?'

'They call me monkey.'

'Who?'

'White man in train.'

'Tell me everything, Jackson.' Stoffel felt his servant was resisting him. He read bitterness in the stoop of Jackson's shoulders and in the whole profile as he sat up.

'You think I'm telling lie, Master? Black man always tell lie, eh?'

'No, Jackson. I can only help if you tell me everything.' Somehow the white man managed to keep his patience.

'I take children to zoo. Coming back I am reading my night-school book. White men come into train and search everyone. One see me reading and say what's this monkey think he's doing with a book. He tell me stand up, he shouts like it's first time for him to talk to a human being. That's what baboons do when they see man. I am hot and boiling and I catch him by his collar and tie and shake him. Ever see a *marula* tree that's heavy with fruit? That's how I shake him. Other white men take me to place in front, a small room. Everyone there hits me hard. At station they push me out on platform and I fall on one knee. They lift me up and take me to police station. Not in city but far away I don't know where but I see now it must have been Victoria Station. There they charge me with drunken noise. Have you a pound? I say no and I ask them they must ring you, they say if I'm cheeky they will hell me up and then they hit and kick me again. They let me go and I walk many miles to hospital. I'm in pain.' Jackson paused, bowing his head lower.

When he raised it again he said, 'I lose letter from my father with my beautiful pictures.'

Stoffel sensed agony in every syllable, in every gesture of the hand. He had read the same story so many times in newspapers and had never given it much thought.

He told Jackson to lie in bed, and for the first time in four years he called a doctor to examine and treat his servant. He had always sent him or taken him to hospital.

For four years he had lived with a servant and had never known more about him than that he had two children living with his mother-in-law, and a wife. Even then they were such distant abstractions — just names representing some persons, not human flesh and blood and heart and mind.

And anger came up in him to muffle the cry of shame, to shut out the memory of recent events that was battering on the iron bars he had built up in himself as a means of protection. There were things he would rather not think about. And the heat of his anger crowded them out. What next? He didn't know. Time, time, time, that's what he needed to clear the whole muddle beneath the fog that rose thicker and thicker with the clash of currents from the past and the present. Time, time . . .

And then Stoffel Visser realised he did not want to think, to feel. He wanted to do something . . . Jackson would want a day off to go to his father . . . Sack Jackson? No. Better continue treating him as a name, not as another human being. Let Jackson continue as a machine to work for him. Meantime, he must do his duty — dispatch the commission's report. That was definite, if nothing else was. He was a white man, and he must be responsible. To be white and to be responsible were one and the same thing . . .

He and the Cat

Take it to a lawyer. That's what my friend told me to do. Now, I had never had occasion to have anything to do with lawyers. Mention of lawyers always brought to my mind pictures of courts, police: terrifying pictures. Although I was in trouble, I wondered why it should be a lawyer who would help me. However, my friend gave me the address.

And from that moment my problem loomed larger. It turned in my mind. On the night before my visit to the solicitor, my heart was full of feelings of hurt. My soul fed on fire and scalding water. I'd tell the lawyer; I'd tell him everything that had gnawed inside me for several days.

I went up the stairs of the high buildings. Whenever I met a man I imagined that he was the lawyer and all but started to pour out my trouble. On the landing I met a boy with a man's head and face and rather large ears and lips. I told him I had come to see Mr B., the lawyer. Very gently, he told me to go into the waiting room and wait my turn with the others. I was disappointed. I had wanted to see Mr B., tell him everything, and get the lawyer's cure for it. To be told to wait . . .

They were sitting in the waiting room, the clients, ranged round the walls — about twenty of them, like those dolls ready to be bowled over at a merry-go-round fair. It didn't seem that I'd get enough time to recite the whole thing — how it all started, grew into something big, and was threatening to crush me — with so many people waiting. The boy with the man's head and face and large ears came in at intervals to call the next person. I knew what I'd do: I'd go over the whole problem in my mind, so that I could even say it backwards. The lawyer must miss nothing, nothing whatever.

But in the course of it all my eyes wandered about the room: the people, the walls, the ceiling, the furniture. A bare, unattractive room: the arms of the chairs had scratches on them that might have been made with a pin by someone who was tired of waiting. Against the only stretch of wall that was free of chairs for clients, a man of about fifty sat at a table sealing envelopes. From a picture on the wall behind him — the only picture in the room — a cat with green eyes looked down as if supervising his work. For some reason I couldn't fathom, a small school globe stood on the table. It suggested that the man sealing the envelopes might start spinning the globe to show a class that the earth is round and turns on its axis.

Once you start to make an effort to think, a thousand-and-one things come into your head. You would think of the previous night's adventure, perhaps; and then your girl friend might force herself into the front line; then you would begin on another trail. You might come back, as I did now, and look at

the cat in front of you or the man at the table or the
clients, one by one. For a fleeting moment the cat
would seem to move. Then it would take up its
former position, its whiskers aggressively proclaiming
that you were a fool to have imagined it in motion.

You watched the frantic movements of a fly
against the windowpane, fussing to get through at the
top when the bottom was open. You looked beyond
to the tall buildings of the city. The afternoon heat
became so oppressive that your head was just a
jumble box. You didn't even hear the boy with a
man's face and large ears call 'Next one!' You seemed
to float on the stagnant air in the room, and to be no
more Sello or Temba in flesh, waiting in a room, but
a creature in the no-time of feeling and thought.

The man at the table continued with his
mechanical work. He, too, seemed to want to escape
from drudgery, for he spoke to two or three clients
near him. And he chuckled often, showing a benignly
toothless mouth. He delighted in bringing out an
aphorism or proverb after every four or five
sentences. 'Our sages say that the only thing you have
that's surely your own is what you've already eaten,
he-he-he'; 'A city is beautiful from afar, but approach
it and it disappoints you, he-he-he.'

The clients talked in groups, discussing various
things. A man was found dead near Shanty Town,
killed by a train, perhaps . . . 'Now, look at me; I've
three sons. Do you think any one of them cares to
bring home a penny? They just feed and sleep and
don't care where the food comes from.'

The man at the table said: 'What I always say is
that as soon as you allow a child to go to a dance,
you've lost her.'

'Try to catch a passing wind — hugh!' 'He cannot

go far; they'll catch him.' . . . 'Imagine it — her husband not six months in his grave, poor man, and she takes off her mourning. That's the reward a good husband gets!'

'Our sages say a herd of cattle led by a cow always falls into the ditch . . . Listen to her always, as long as you know you have the last word . . . '

'I once met a man . . . ' ' . . . Potatoes? Everything is costly these days. Even a woman has gone up in price when you want to marry.' . . . 'Only God knows when we are ever to go where we want to at any time' . . . 'Are we not here because of money? Do not we walk the streets and ride on trains and buses because of money? Is money not the thing that drives us in our wanderings?'

'Death is in the leg; we walk with it, he-he-he.'

'You have not been to Magaba, you say? Then you know nothing. Women selling fruit, everyone as red as the ground on which they stand; men and women just one with the red earth; salted meat roasting on the grid to be sold; red dust swirling above, people dashing this way and that like demons scorching in a fire — something like a dream.'

The man at the table laughed again and said, 'But horns that are put on you never stick on — so don't worry about gossip.'

'We've fallen upon evil days when a girl can beat her mother-in-law.' . . . 'It's the first I've seen for many years. In my day a cow could give birth to a donkey if such a thing happened.' . . . 'Oh, everybody beats everybody these days; we've lost, lost.' 'But we can't go back.'

'I'll know it's a zebra when I see the stripes.' This from the table.

'He reads too much; the white doctors say his brain

is fermenting.'

'Even the eagle comes down to earth.' Another proverb.

'You and I have never had the chance to go to school, so we must send our children; they'll read and write for us.' . . . 'Didn't you hear? They say the poor man was screaming and trying to run away before he died. He was crying and saying a mountain of sins was standing in his way.' . . . 'Yes, his wife stood by his bed, and he said to her, he says, "Selope, take care of my son; now give me water to drink. This is the last time," he says, "I shall ever ask you to do anything for me." '

The boy with the man's face and large ears came to tell us that two white men had gone into Mr B.'s office. There was a moment's silence. The man at the table nodded several times. The cat glowered at him with green eyes and almost live whiskers. The fly must have found its way out. The heat was becoming a problem to reckon with.

'How many times have I come here,' said an old woman to no one in particular. 'In the meantime, my grandchildren are starving. Their good-for-nothing father has not sent them money since the law separated him from my daughter.' Deeper silence. A few people frowned at the old woman as the birds are said to have done when they were about to attack the owl. A few others seemed to be telling themselves that they weren't hearing what they were hearing.

'Where does the old mother come from?' It was someone next to her. Once he had started he went on with a string of questions to get her off the track.

And so the people went on patching up. During all this time I had got my facts straight in my head. Several times I had imagined myself in front of Mr B.:

a short man with tired eyes (I always envisioned the lawyer as small in stature). I had told him everything. Now, as I sat here in the waiting room, I already knew I'd be relieved; the burden would fall off as soon as I should have seen and talked to Mr B. I was so sure. It couldn't be otherwise.

There was little talking now. Fools! I thought. Their inner selves were smarting and curdling with past hurts (like mine); they were aching to see Mr B., to tell him their troubles. Yet here they were, pretending they had suspended their anxiety. Here they were, trying to rip this wave of heat and scatter it by so much gas talk: babbling away over things that didn't concern them, to cover the whirlpool of their own troubles. What was beneath these eddies and bubbles dancing and bursting on a heat wave? — someone else's possessions, flouting of the law, unfaithfulness, the forbidden tree? And the man at the table: what right had he to pronounce those aphorisms and proverbs, old as the language of man, and bleached like a brown shirt that has become a dirty white? What right had he to chuckle like that, as though he regarded us as a shopkeeper does his customers? Next one . . . the next one . . . Next!

I was left alone with the man and the cat. My heart gave a hard beat when my mind switched back to what had brought me to the lawyer. Give it to a lawyer, my friend had said confidently, as though I merely had to press an electric switch. He'll help you out of the mud. A damned good solicitor. You give him the most difficult case and he'll talk you free . . . Yes, I'd tell him everything; all that troubled my waking and sleeping hours. Then everything would be all right. I felt it would be so.

'The big man is very busy today, eh?' observed the

man at the table.

'Yes,' I said, mechanically.

My attention was drawn to the whole setting once more: a plain, unpretentious room with oldish chairs; the school globe; the pile of letters and envelopes; the man; and the picture of the cat.

An envelope fell to the floor. He bent down to take it up. I watched his large hands feel about for it, fumbling. Then the hand came upon the object, but with much more weight than a piece of paper warranted. Even before he came up straight on his chair I saw it clearly. The man at the table was blind, stone blind. As my eyes were getting used to the details, after my mind had thus been jolted into confused activity, I understood. Here was a man sealing envelopes, looking like a drawing on a flat surface. Perhaps he was flat and without depth, like a gramophone disc; too flat even to be hindered by the heat, the boredom of sitting for hours doing the same work; by too many or too few people coming. An invincible pair, he and the cat glowering at him, scorning our shames and hurts and the heart, seeming to hold the key to the immediate imperceptible and the remote unforeseeable.

I went in to see Mr B., a small man (as I had imagined) with tired eyes but an undaunted face. I told him everything from beginning to end.

The Barber of Bariga

'Ha ha ha! Na be fonny worl' dees. A mahn mos'
always have to lawwe ay-gain un ay-gain.'

Anofi turned the round head to the left with his
large hand as if he were spinning a toy. The head was
indeed getting out of hand as Bashiru laughed
riotously. And he continued to plough through his
client's hair with his clippers. Anofi came to Bashiru's
house each month to 'barb' his hair, as they say.

'Who be your woman dees mont', chief?' Anofi
asked with tight-jawed grimness.

'Ha ha ha! A yong yong tender t'ing, my frien'.'

'Bot you no be happy for your t'ree wive?'

'Yes, bot I wan' be more happy. You know what
oyingbo say: he say de more de merry merrier
merriest. Now no be vex my frien' Anofi, no be vex. I
see for mirror na be so.'

The barber was annoyed indeed to see the lines of
his frown on the forehead. He pushed his client's
head to one side with a fury-driven thumb.

'No, no be vex me. I jos' be feah.'

'For wettin' you feah?'

'She be married.'

'Y-yes. Bot no be worry she no be ole she be fresh un quick un lawvely as anyt'ing. Yes, yes, clever to make lawve and stupid for up deer.' He indicated his head.

'Das for why I be feah, chief. Why no leave um de married wawn? Na be plenty woman wit'out man for dis Lagos.' Anofi drew breath through his teeth to make a hissing noise as a sign of disgust.

Another shove of the head with his finger.

'Take time take time, no be vex for my head, Anofi.'

'Who's she?'

'A secret.'

There was a brief pause.

'People be talkin' for dis in Bariga,' Anofi said.

'What people — wettin' dey talk?'

'You un som' woman.'

'Dey say who?'

Anofi knew Bashiru's head very well; round with an eternal pimple or blackhead on the side near the ear and an old scar in the form of a slight dent in the flesh of the skull. It was an easy head to handle for a cut. Often when Anofi propelled his clippers through the hair, he seemed to fondle the head, pushing it deftly this way and that with his thumb or forefinger. The barber seemed to own the head, as if there were a point of identity with it, as if he would be hurt if someone else gave it a haircut. As his clippers nibbled down the slopes, he seemed conscious of his physical ease and the good job being done of his cut.

The barber put the finishing touches, and Bashiru looked tidy. He grunted approval, like a purring over-sized cat that is being stroked, when Anofi held the mirror behind for him to see the trimming effects at the back of his head.

'T'ank you,' Bashiru said, giving the barber three shillings and adjusting his *agbada*. *'Odabo,* sah — remain in peace.'

Anofi went out into the sun. He knew his father would be entertaining the waiting customers in his shop with some of his funny stories.

For the last ten years or so Anofi's father came to sit in the shop while the barber worked. The old man featured in his memory mostly in the posture in which he sat on the bench in the shop: one leg bent and resting almost entirely on the bench; the other bent leg shooting up vertically so that he could plant his elbow on the knee and prop up the head with his open palm. The old man often struck that pose when he was sure what he said would be regarded as expert counsel or a statement that could brook no argument. He was more often sure than not, and he seldom failed to raise an argument with the clients. Each morning he came into the shop through the back door, shuffled his feet to the front door, looking cool in his *buba,* and surveyed the street life. Then he turned round and went to take his post on the bench.

Often Anofi's old man spoke in a monotone, apparently not caring whether anyone was listening or not. Or he chewed away at his kola nut, his jaws moving like a goat's. Indeed there was something goatlike about his face, altogether; he also sneezed as weakly and coughed as fussily as a goat. When he smiled to deride an argument, he would emphasize this by stretching out his lips so as to push out bits of kola nut with the inside lining of his cheeks so they should not escape the onslaught of his scattered molars. In the process, his rusty-coloured front teeth came into full view, looking like the remaining few pillars of a demolished building.

Anofi went on with his work, seldom turning round to engage in conversation with his father. When he was working, his father hovered somewhere in his subconscious or somewhere on the fringe of awareness. On one of the few occasions when father and son exchanged ideas, the older man said in the middle of the morning, 'I am sure if you collected all the hair you cut off and found someone to buy it, you would get rich.' He chewed his stick for cleaning his teeth.

'Rich — how, Papa?'

'I don't know why the white man cannot use people's hair.'

'Why, Papa?'

'The white people use sheep's hair, the hair of wild animals.'

Now he moved his stick, which had split into broomlike bristles at the end, in vertical strokes. All this gave his words a sarcastic ring he might not have intended them to contain.

'Are you joking, Papa?'

'No.'

'But people's hair is so dirty.' Anofi's body twitched from a sensation of disgust.

'The white man can do many things. He can make machines to wash the hair. The white man seems to be clever.'

'Why always white man white man? Cannot the black man do these things?' Anofi said in spite of his disgust.

'What machines have we ever made?'

'But we use them very well. You, Papa, you are like the woman who came out of the office of the dentist and said to us who were waiting, "Oyingbo — the white man is wonderful, he has made things to take out a tooth without pain." And you know who had taken out her tooth? A black woman doctor. Oho, you are like that.'

There was a moment of silence while the client was shaking off hair from his clothes, slapping the back of his neck several times. Then he straightened up. Looking at Anofi's father he took out a ballpoint pen. 'Look,' the customer said. He pressed the end of the protruding stick in so that the writing tip shot out. He pressed the clip and the tip disappeared. He repeated the operation a few times and then said: 'Na whitemahn na wonderful – o. Look wettin' he make!' He smiled and walked out, leaving Anofi in fits of laughter from which he only recovered several minutes later. Papa looked upset and, to express it, he noisily sucked air through the central gap between the top biting teeth in order to push in a morsel of kola nut.

Most times Anofi said very little, and looked exasperatingly unruffled. It seemed that he never wanted to stir up things. He seemed incapable of nervous tension, of anger or malice.

He saw much of what happened in the street through the window. Masqueraders passed by, frightening children and beating drums, sprawling all over the place and prancing as if they itched to do something desperate or exciting. 'They are looking for fun, and they will get it,' Anofi would say to himself. Wedding and funeral processions passed by, and groups of women in party uniform – on all these, he seldom voiced a comment. He consciously or unconsciously refused to be emotionally involved, seeming to despise the whole show. He did not, however, despise it. He liked much of the music booming out of the loudspeaker in the opposite shop where they played gramophone records or had the radio on throughout the day.

The current high-life favourite was 'Corner Love'. The vocalist said how much he disliked 'corner love' and mistrusted it. He warned the young woman against the lad who drew her onto a street corner to propose love. 'I no like corner-corner love', the singer insisted forebodingly. One customer thought the singer was wasting his time and vocal energy, because 'na be no corner-lawve for dis Lagos, a-ah!! He jos tok-tok for not'ing cawm ot for his head. If to say you hask 'im he woul'n't know.'

One Saturday morning a car drove down the street with a white couple in it. Anofi was moving towards his signboard EXPERT BARBAR to adjust it (the 'r' in *expert* perched on top of the 'e' and the 't' with a sign to indicate that the signwriter had forgotten it, or simply had not known it should be there). He saw the car stop at the crossroads and a cyclist drive into a wedge between the car and wall. Just then, the car moved again. To Anofi, who had stopped short in front of his signboard, it was quite clear that the cyclist was going to be in trouble. The bumper caught the spokes of the front wheel. The rider was unseated. The rider was suspended in air for a split second, his *agbada* ballooning as he made the forced landing, with a cry, 'What ees wrong!' The driver pulled up short in the middle of the cross-street on sensing the trouble, by which time Anofi had a seizure of torrential laughter, such as he was never known to have the capacity for. He did not move away from the signboard, but clung to one of the two poles holding it up, as if he were afraid he would take off.

In a short time a number of people had gathered at

the place of the accident. The white man was having
an argument with the cyclist who was claiming
money for repairs. Always people gathered around
some place where something was happening that was
not daily routine: a man changing a tyre; a petrol
attendant checking tyres; a motorist stopping to
drink tea out of a flask, and so on. Whenever there
had been an accident, the crowd had many
observations and opinions to air, far more of the
latter than the former.

The white man soon felt overwhelmed by the
presence of the chattering and murmuring crowd and
anger was beginning to choke him. The cyclist was
now clearly crying. Small children pointed fingers at
him and giggled. He looked at his *agbada* in between
complaining and claiming compensation.

Suddenly the white woman came out of the car.
She seemed beside herself with fury. She started to
drag her husband back to the car shouting to the
cyclist the while: 'Go to the police then, go to the
police and have us arrested, but you're getting not a
farthing out of us!' She paused as the husband was
not coming readily. Then again, 'Why don't you go
and report the matter if you're not satisfied? You
came in between the car and the fence.' Dropping her
voice a little, 'Let's go, Andrew, let's go. Come, come
into the car. We've got to go, we haven't got time to
be wasting listening to this silly talk.'

The man Andrew put the brakes on somewhere in
his legs. He was tall and thin, and his small head was
swaying above all the others. His face was a deep pink
from unchecked perspiration. He was also suppressing
an itching sensation in one of his now wet armpits. He
felt if he scratched it now it would blunt the edge of
the point he was trying to make; like suddenly

coughing in the middle or at the beginning of a venomous phrase during a quarrel or a reprimand. Perhaps he did not want to feel that he had arbitrarily decided that he was in the right if in fact the other man was. And then there was a chance that they might both be wrong or right. Moreover, the other man's crying act was embarrassing him.

'No go say I um seely,' the cyclist barked.

'I think you're just being silly,' the woman insisted.

'Joo can't abuse me like dat, a-ah! It's un insolt. I say joo can't abuse me. Um not your stewart.'

'No, you're too silly to be anybody's stewart.'

'A-Ah, she's abusing me ay-gain, a-ah! Do you hear-hear-ah?' Then he broke into Yoruba, definitely appealing to the sensibilities of the crowd.

'Slap her!' someone shouted.

'If not to say she's a woo-man, I coul' 'ave slapped her. But what is she besides — just *oyingbo.*'

The woman, realizing that Andrew was not obeying her command, left the crowd and walked towards Anofi, who was still standing by the sign-board. He had only just recovered from his fit of laughing.

'You were looking at us as we were coming on, what did you see? Please tell them what you saw.' *Them* referred to the crowd, just as if she had begun to accept the incident as a communal concern.

They looked in the direction of the barber-shop.

Anofi shrugged his narrow shoulders, shook his head, 'I never know, I never see not'ing, I mean moch.' And he walked into his shop.

The woman gave a deep sigh and she said to Andrew again, 'Let's go, it'll do us no good talking like this.'

'Let's give the man ten shillings for his repairs.'

'Over my dead body!'

He took out the money and walked towards the cyclist with his arm outstretched.

'Andrew, come here! Don't just give away money like that!'

He was just barely able to hear the cyclist say: 'T'ank you. Na we be frien's now.' There was loud cheering from the group of people as though an armistice had been declared. He went to join his protesting wife in the car, feeling anything but heroic.

'Between that wretched lying barber and your stupid self,' she said, 'the devil alone knows how these people mean to build a nation.'

'That's a problem for the nation-builders, darling. Besides, how can you be sure that simply because a man was looking at us, as you say the barber was doing, he must have seen what happened?'

'Oh he knows he did.' She looked in the direction of the shop door, and saw that Anofi was looking at them. 'The African always wins when those of his kind are in authority.'

'It's *our* turn to learn that lesson, darling.'

And the car shot forward.

There must have been several times when Anofi himself could not say whether he had actually seen what he thought he had seen, or whether in his perpetual mood of detachment he told himself that he was not seeing what he was seeing. When a blind beggar came to his door, he dug his hand into his pocket, took out a coin and, as if in a dream, walked to the door and dropped it in the beggar's enamel bowl. Three blind women might stop at his door with children on their backs. They would wail their incantations to Allah with heartrending effect, so that Anofi's father's jaws pounded harder on the kola nut and, with the aid of his tongue, drew air through the side teeth to hiss his bewilderment and pride. Anofi, for his part, usually went to the door in a kind of tremor to tell the party to move away. On approaching them, he saw their grey, lifeless and solicitous eyes quivering beneath the eyelids, and he saw their red teeth and the footprints of small-pox on their faces. And something deep-deep down in the pit of his stomach would stir. He would give something and return quickly to his customer.

'These beggars!' a customer would sometimes say. 'Day give too moch troble, a-ah! Dey be blind nu dey go born piccin, a-ah! Foolish nort'erner woman.' Anofi would keep mute, some chord inside him still quivering.

About a month after the last haircut Anofi gave Bashiru, the man of property, a large man entered the shop and literally threw himself into a bench near Anofi's father. He was quite out of breath. Anofi's old father felt very tiny near such a mountain of man, and it irritated him.

'Have you ever hear soch a t'ing Anofi,' Okeke puffed out. 'I go kill him true, believe me I go slaughter dat man. He goes ay-bout wit' a dead title, dead-dead title and rascally t'ings.'

'Who's dat?' Anfi asked.

'Bashiru.'

'Wettin' he don'?'

'He t'ink becos na he be rich,' and he began ticking the items off his sausage-like fingers, 'he got plenty moni, plenty houses, plenty upstairs, plenty wives, plenty piccin, plenty farm, so he can't keep his man inside for pants for his wives only. Even he take oder people's wives too.'

'Bot wettin he don?'

'Look um. His grand-dad don' eat his chief's title. His dad don' try to force it out to be made chief un he don' fail. Bot his dad was clever un he don' take oder people's houses un moni. He don' t'ief t'ief everyt'ing un now his son Bashiru take de blod of t'ief from his dad un t'ief t'ief wife un moni un houses all over now he be fat un rich . . . '

'Wettin he don'?'

'Foolish mah, I tell him what Bashiru don' don' un he still hask what he don', a-ah! Na you be no idi-awt, Anofi.' He rose to take the chair for a cut. 'Bashiru be tryin' to t'ief my wife.'

'Your wife na she be wantin' to be t'iefed?'

'You make me vex, Anofi. How can my wife want to be t'iefed? Don't tell me you don't know ay-bout it. Everybody in Bariga knows it.'

The answer startled Anofi. Bashiru had boasted about his latest exploit, but he could never have thought that Okeke's wife would be so foolish as to be seduced.

'Moni ay-gain, you see for dat? Now I know Bashiru has been takin' my wife when I'm wo'kin' in town. Believe me I go kill dat mahn. I no sleep at night becos of wawry, I don't chop becos of wawry and Bashiru chop chop bellyful becos he no wawry.'

'Please no be too vex I beg you Okeke. No be good to kill -o. Jos' beat him das all.'

Okeke's neck stiffened, and Anofi had to wait a few seconds before he could turn the man's head to a desired angle. So he did it, that Bashiru, he thought. Okeke's voice filled him with unhappy thoughts.

For a reason he could not explain he felt he was being sucked into the affair between the three persons. He did not know what was happening to him, and he did not seem to have the power to resist being sucked in. When Okeke left, he and his father looked at each other for a spell, as if their thoughts had found a confluence and were rushing down the same mainstream, and there was nothing more to say about it.

When two days later a message came to Anofi that Bashiru had died by accident at a wedding, he sensed evil in the air. He was called to come and shave Bashiru's head to prepare him for burial, according to the rules of a religious cult to which the deceased belonged. He soon found himself in the death room. The group of people in there made way for him to pass and kneel beside the corpse. He sat down and put the head on his lap. The thought that this head, the contour lines of which he knew so well, was now like a stone, made him shiver. When there was still a patch of hair left, Anofi's clippers struck against something hard. He ran his clippers against the obstacle once more and the sound told him it was metal. He shaved around it until it emerged: the head of a nail that told him in no doubtful terms that it was a long thick one.

With a sudden movement the barber lifted up the head onto the pillow on the floor, jumped up and said to the people in the room: 'Why you no go tell me dat dis man was killed de way of a t'ief?' He did not wait for a reply but dashed out of the house. Outside he stood still in the street. He stood like a man who, feeling a fever coming on, seems to be tuning in to the mechanism that is the body in an attempt to feel the throb of it, perhaps to reassure himself. Then he walked on.

Dusk was creeping in, but from the elevated end of the street where Anofi was, the rusted iron roofs of

Bariga's houses were still clearly defined in all their recklessly uneven outlines. Shopkeepers and petty street traders were pumping their pressure lamps. Soon lights would be exploding in various places from candles, pressure lamps and other manual contraptions. People coming in from Lagos where they worked. Anofi only faintly heard the continuous roar of human noises, absorbed as he was in other things.

'Make we walk togeder,' someone said coming from a side-street.

Anofi merely looked at Okeke and walked on.

'You cawmin' from Bashiru's house?'

'Yes.' He was not sure whether he wanted to talk to someone or not. 'You don' kill man, Okeke.'

'Som' people dey don' kill um.'

'You don' kill man, Okeke,' Anofi repeated, as if his mind pounded at regular intervals, heedless of any other sound.

'Som' people not me. But he don' die way na he want.'

'You don' kill a *mahn! A mahn,* you don't take de life of a man to buy de lawve of a woman. Na be what kind of lawve dis? Not to say you can't beat your woman for stick, you savvy? You can beat woman un kick her if she sleep for anoder man's bed, beat her un send her to hospitule. Na she got madness for head un hotness for flesh you can kick dem ot, dis madness and hotness. Not to kill anoder man a-ah.' He looked straight ahead of him all the time, as if there were no one beside him.

His insistence irritated Okeke, but it also made him uncomfortable. But he wasn't going to be frightened out of his course. All the time they walked on without looking at each other.

'Das how dey kill t'iefman for my contry,' Okeke said gloatingly but with self-confidence. 'Bashiru don' t'ief som't'ing for some'body.'

'Un you don' send um to kill.'

'Jos savvy me, Anofi, I no wan' no palaver me son of Okeke. I hate big mahn strong mahn who eats from hand of de poor people, take wife for people wi'out no moni, fat mahn who chop chop bellyful moni dat is oder people's own. Now he t'inks he's God almighty un he wan' chop oder people's wives, a-ah!'

'Na you hate him becos he was rich and fat not becos he don' t'ief your woman?'

'Is for same t'ing Anofi. You no be borned yester-night. Is samet'ing. Poor man t'ief small small becos he's afraid for big moni, rich man t'ief big becos he got protec-shon un he buy police*mahn.*'

'Un your wife be fool woman un cheap if she stand for de middle of de road for him to jomp on top of her.'

'If not to say you be my friend' I coul' 'ave feel vex. Bot even you know Bashiru is not jos any cock. He got moni and no woman fit for say no when she moni in front of her eyes.'

'How you t'ink you escape for police?'

'Moni for his pocket un he shot op for mout' and let his tongue sleep.'

'Even you don' get rich now, you? Okeke, dis is a big terrible t'ing. Even I nevah know what I go say for police an dey hask me . . . '

'Only what you saw for inside, his big dead head. Make you say not'ing pass dat at-all-at-all-at-all.'

'Why?'

'Becos Bashiru he don't make lawve for you wife too, idi-awt! Wake op! She waitin' to tell you for house. See you nex' tomorrow.'

Okeke left him.

Many things began to make sense to him. He saw his wife's beauty for what it was. Indeed she leapt into his field of awareness as she had seldom ever done in her physical form. This rediscovery of her loveliness fused with the anger in him so that the world around him seemed so small, so overcrowded.

He made a detour without meaning to, often running into dead ends. He felt numb. 'To-morrow,' he said aloud in his language and with an air of finality, 'we must go away from this place. The whole house.'

And as Anofi walked on, radio music exploded from a nearby shop and set his nerves quivering:

No moni, no bus,
Even na you be clever
        pass every-wawn:
No moni, no bus.

Bariga is a village in Lagos, Nigeria, where the author first taught, before he moved north. The dialogue is in pidgin English, an urban dialect that mixes English and vernacular words and phrases. It does not adhere to the English sentence structure. People from different language groups communicate in pidgin among illiterate and semi-literate people or between these and literate types. It is a highly inventive and expressive dialect in which the speaker can take liberties with syntax and vocabulary, although one regional pidgin may vary from another throughout West Africa. There are other variations in the French-speaking countries of West Africa.

A Ballad of Oyo

Ishola (also called Mama-Jimi because her first son was Jimi) found a tramp on her counter slab at Oyo's central market, where she took her stand each day to sell vegetables and fruit. Furiously she poked the grimy bundle with a broom to tell him a few things he had better hear: *there are several other places where he could sleep; she sells food off this counter, not fire-wood — like him; so he thought to lie on a cool slab on a hot night, eh? — Why does he not sleep under a running tap?* And so on. With a sense of revulsion she washed the counter.

These days, when market day began, it also meant that Ishola was going to have to listen to her elder sister's endless prattling during which she spun words and words about the younger sister being a fool to keep a useless husband like Balogun in food and clothing. Off and on, for three months, Ishola had tried to fight against the decision to tell Balogun to go look for another wife while she went her own way. Oh, why did her sister have to blabber like this? Did her sister think that she, Ishola, liked being kicked about by her man? Her sister might well go on like this, but she could not divine the burning questions that churned inside Ishola.

That is right, Ishola, her sister who sold rice next to her, would say. *You are everybody's fool, are you not? Lie still like that and let him come and sit and play drums on you and go off and get drunk on palm wine, come back and beat you, scatter the children — children of his palm-wine-stained blood* (spitting), *like a hawk landing among chicks, then you have no one to blame only your stupid head* (pushing her other breast forcibly into her baby's mouth for emphasis). *How long has he been giving you so much pain like this? How long are you going to try to clean a pig that goes back into the mud? You are going to eat grass very soon, you will tell me — and do not keep complaining to me about his ways if my advice means nothing to you.*

And so goes the story of Ishola, Ishola who was called Mama-Jimi, a mother of three children. Slender, dark-and-smooth-skinned, with piercing eyes that must have seen through dark nights.

Day and night the women of Oyo walk the black road, the road of tarmac, to and from the market. They can be seen walking, riding the dawn, walking into sunrise; figures can be seen, slender as twilight; their feet feel every inch of the tarmac, but their wares press down on the head and the neck takes the strain, while the hip and legs propel the body forward. A woman here, a woman there in the drove has her arm raised in a loop, a loop of endurance, to support the load, while the other arm holds a suckling child in a loop, a loop of love. They must walk fast, almost at a trot, so that they may not feel the pain of the weight so much.

The week before Mama-Jimi had started for Oyo Market, her body feeling the seed of another child grow that had not yet begun to give her sweet torment, bitter ecstasy in the stomach. The night before he left, her husband had told her he was going to the north to see his other wives. He would come back — when? *When he was full of them and they of him,* Mama-Jimi knew. *When he should have made sure that the small trade each was doing went well,* he said.

Mama-Jimi looked at his shadow quivering on the wall in the light of the oil lamp as he stooped over her, and loneliness swept over her in a flood. They loved and they remained a promontory rising above the flood. And Mama-Jimi again took her place in the order of things: one of three wives giving all of her to one she loved and taking what was given by her man with a glad heart. Oyo will always be Oyo; whatever happens to it, the market will always be there, come rain, come blood, come malaria.

It was the week before, only the week before, when the rain caught the market women on the tarmac to market. The sky burst and the rain caught the market women on the tarmac to market. The sky burst and the rain came down with power. It rumbled down the road in rivulets. Mama-Jimi felt the load inside become heavy, knotting up beneath her navel. Her feet became heavy, the hips failed to twist. But she tried to push on. She could see the others way ahead through the grey of the rain. Mama-Jimi's thoughts were on the market, the market of Oyo: she must reach it. For if she should fall, she thought, or feel sicker, other women were there.

But the woman sagged and fell and dragged herself

out of the road. She felt the blood oozing, warm and cold. A life was running out of her, she was sure of it.

A life dead just as soon as born and sprouting . . .

Two women found her on the roadside, cold, wet.

Whispers bounced and rebounded at the market that Mama-Jimi was dead, dead, Mama-Jimi was gone, gone in the rain. But it was not as whispers told it.

Did she know it was there?

Ehe, she did, she told me so.

And her man gone to the north, a-ah? So it is said.

Are they going to call him? They must. Only yesterday night we were together and she was glad she was going to give her man a third child.

To die when your people are far far away from you, a-ah!

We are most of us strangers here.

It is true.

This was a week before, and the market at Oyo jingles and buzzes and groans, but it goes on as it has done for many years before when the first Alafin came here.

You know what the market is like every morning, not so? Babbling tongues, angry tongues, silent tongues. Down there a woman was suckling a baby while she sold. Near to Ishola a woman was eating *gari* and *okaran* and gravy out of a coloured enamel bowl. Someone else next to her handled her sales for her. As the heat mounted a lad was pouring water on bunches of lettuce to keep them from wilting and thus refusing to be sold. But the lad seemed to be wilting himself, because as soon as he leaned back against a pole, sleep seized him and his head tilted back helplessly like a man having a shave in a barber's chair.

The mouth opened and the lettuce lost its importance for a while. Mostly *oyingbo* — white people — came to buy lettuce. On and off while he slept, someone sprinkled water on his face. This seldom jolted him out of his stupor. He merely ran his hand over his face, stared at the lettuce and then poured water on it. Some fat women opposite Ishola's counter were shouting and one seldom knew whether they were angry or simply zealous. They also splashed water over the pork they were selling so as to keep away blue flies that insisted on sitting on it. All the would-be buyers who stood at the pork counter fingered the pieces: they lifted them up, turned them round, put them back, picked them up again. There was no exchange of smiles here.

Ten shillings, said the pork woman who herself seemed to have been wallowing in grease.

Four shillings, suggested the customer.

Eight shillings last.

Five (taking it and putting it back as if disgusted).

Seven las' price.

With a long-drawn sound between the teeth to signify disgust, the customer left. The pork woman looked at her fellow-vendor, as if to say, stupid customers!

Oyingbo women did not buy meat at these markets.

They said they were appalled by the number of hands that clutched at it. They bought imported meat in the provision stores at prices fixed seemingly to annoy expatriates. One missionary woman had been known to bring a scale for the vendor to weigh the meat in order to get her money's worth. What, she had exclaimed, you don't weigh meat in this market? Ridiculous! The meat women had looked baffled.

The next time the missionary brought her own balance. This time *they* thought something was ridiculous, and they laughed to show it. Even after weighing a piece, she found that she still had to haggle and bargain. Enthusiasm had flagged on her part, and after this, she only came to the market to rescue some of the lettuce and parsley from continual drenching and to buy fruit.

So did the other white women. One of them turned round in answer to a shout from a vendor. Custumah, custumah! She approached Ishola's counter where there were heaps of carrots and tomatoes. She was smiling, as one is expected to do from behind a counter.

Nice car-*rot* madam.

How much?

Shilling (picking up a bunch).

Sixpence.

No madam, shilling (smiling).

Sixpence.

Ha-much madam wan' pay? (with no smile).

All right, seven pence.

Ni'pence.

Seven.

No 'gree, madam (smiling).

The customer realized that she had come to the end of the road. She yielded, but not before saying, ninepence is too much for these.

A-ah madam. If not to say madam she buy for me many times I coul' 'ave took more moni for you.

Towards sunset Ishola packed up. She had made up her mind to go to Bab Dejo, the president of the court of the local authority. She firmly believed that the old man had taken a bribe. Either her father-in-law or Balogun himself, her delinquent husband,

could have offered it. This, she believed, must be the
reason why the court would not hold a hearing of her
case against her husband. Twice Ishola had asked him
to hear her case. Each time the old man said something to delay it. The old fox, she thought. This time,
she fixed simply on putting five pounds in front of
the president. He cannot refuse so much money,
Ishola thought. But go back to that animal of a
husband, never — *no more, he is going to kill me one
of these days I do not want to die I do not want to
die for nothing I want to work for my children I want
to send them to school I do not want them to grow
old on the market place and die counting money and
finding none. Baba Dejo just take the money he must
listen to my case and let the law tell Balogun to leave
me alone with the children and go his way I will go
mine I know his father has gone and bribed him to
keep the matter out of the court and why? — because
he does not want to lose his son's children and
because — I do not know he is very fond of me he has
always stood up for me against his son — yes he loves
me but I am married to his son not to him and his
love does not cure his son's self-made madness. Lijadu
loves me and I want him let my heart burst into many
pieces if he does not take me as his wife I want him
because he has such a pure heart.*

Ishola was thinking of the day Lijadu came to
fetch her in his car and they went to Ijebude for that
weekend of love and heartbreaks: heartbreaks
because she was someone else's wife, someone who
did not care for her and even then had gone to Warri
without telling her. Now Lijadu was ready to give
Balogun the equivalent of the bride price he had paid
to Ishola's parents and so release her to become his
wife. Balogun and his father had refused Lijadu's

money.

Just what irritates me so, Ishola thought. I could burst into a hundred parts so much it fills me with anger. So they want to stop me from leaving their useless son, useless like dry leaves falling from a tree. Just this makes me mad and I feel I want to stand in the middle of the road and shout so as everyone can hear me. That man! — live with him again? He beats me he leaves me no money he grows fat on my money he does not care for the children the children of his own own blood from his very own hanging things . . .

I wonder how much the old man will want? The thought flashed across Ishola's mind, like a streak of lightning that rips across the milling clouds, illuminating the sky's commotion all the more.

If your father-in-law Mushin were not my friend, says the president of the court, Dejo, when Ishola tells him the business of her visit, I should not let you come and speak to me on a matter like this. It is to be spoken in court only.

You do not want me to bring it to court sir.

I would do it if —

How much, sir?

Give me what you have, my daughter. He looks disdainful in the face as he says so. It does not please the young woman. He takes five pounds in paper money from her hand.

What is this I hear from your father-in-law, that you want to leave your husband? Ishola feels resentful at the thought that her case must have been chewed dead by these old men. But she presses the lid hard to keep her feelings from bubbling over. I beg that you listen, sir, she says. Balogun beats me he does not work he eats and sleeps he does not care for the children of his own-own blood, sir, he drinks too much palm wine this is too much I have had a long heart to carry him so far but this is the end of every thing no no this is all I can carry.

Is he a man in bed?

Not when he is drunk and that is many times sir. She was looking at the floor at this time.

Hm, that is bad that is bad my child, that is bad. What does he say when you talk to him about his ways?

Nothing, sir. He just listens he listens and just listens that is all.

A man has strange ways and strange thoughts.

There is silence.

So he drinks himself stupid. I know there are certain places in Oyo where you can hear the name of Balogun spoken as if he were something that smells very bad. So he drinks himself stupid until he is too flabby to do his work in bed, a-ah! How many children have you by the way?

Three, sir.

The youngest is how old?

Two years, sir.

If a man gets too drunk to hoe a field another man will and he shall regret, he will see. He seems to be talking to himself: But a man who comes home only as a he-goat on heat, the old man continues, and not as a helper and father is useless. I will tell him that I will tell Balogun that myself. Animals look for food for their mates and their brood, why cannot a man?

You have talked to him twice before, sir,

Oh yes oh yes I have my child I know.

Silence.

But your father-in-law Mushin loves you so much so much my child.

I love him too but I am his son's wife not his.
You speak the truth there.
Silence.
It would break his heart all the same. Look at it whichever way you like. You fill a space left in his heart by the death of his wife and often defiled by the deeds of a worthless son. Dejo's face is one deep shadow of gravity.

I do not like that boy Balogun not one little moment, he goes on, but his father will weep because he holds you like his own-own daughter.

Ishola's head is full of noises and echoes of noises, for she has heard all this a few times before. She has determined her course and she shall not allow her tender sentiments to take her out of it, she mustn't, no, not now. Perhaps after, when tender feelings will be pointless. She still bears a little love for Balogun, but she wants her heart to be like a boulder so as not to give way.

Let me go and call my wife to talk with you more about this, old Dejo says as he leaves the room. As he does so, he stretches out his hand to place a few crumpled notes of money in Ishola's hand, whispering your heart is kind, my child, it is enough that you showed the heart to give, so take it back.

Ishola feels a warm and cold air sweep over and through her. She trembles a little and she feels as if something were dangling in space and must fall soon.

Old Dejo's wife enters, round-bellied: the very presence of life's huge expectation.

But — such an old man, Ishola thinks . . .

I can see it in her eyes Balogun I can see it in her eyes, Mushin said in his son's house one morning. Ishola is going to leave us.

She is at the market now, Papa. She loves me too much to do a foolish thing like that.

When are you going to wake up you useless boy, he gasped, as he had often done before. What kind of creature was given me for a son! What does your mother say from the other world to see you like this!

Balogun poured himself palm wine and drank and drank and drank. I can see the blade of a cutlass coming to slash at my heart, the older man said, I can feel it coming.

Go and rest father, you are tired.

And Balogun walked out into the blazing shimmering sun, stopped to buy cigarettes at a small stall on the roadside and walked on, the very picture of aimlessness.

When are you going to stop fooling like this with Balogun I ask you, Ishola's sister said rasping out as she sat behind her counter. Her baby who was sucking looked up into her face with slight but mute concern in its eyes.

She does not know she does know this woman she . . . will never know she will know what I am made of . . .

I would never allow a man to come stinking of drink near me in the blankets (spitting). I told you long ago to go to court and each time you allow that old Dejo with his fat wife to talk you out of it. Are you a daughter of my father?

Oh what a tiresome tongue sister has . . . You wait you, you just wait . . .

Just a black drunken swine that is what he is. A swine is even better because it can look for rubbish to eat. Balogun does not know what people are he would not go a long way with me no he would not he does not know people. Eat sleep and lay a pile of dung, eat sleep and lay a pile of dung while men of his age group are working: the woman who gave birth to that man . . . !

Sister! Leave that poor woman to lie quiet in her grave!

I will but not that wine-bloated creature called Balogun.

Lijadu must not forget to send Mushin's money of the bride-price . . .

That piece of pork? a customer asked.

Ten shillings.

Five.

Nine.

Six.

No 'gree.

Six and six.

No 'gree.

Six and six.

No 'gree. Eight, las' price.

Seven.

No 'gree.

And the market roar and chatter and laughter and exclamations and smells put together seemed to be a live symphony quite independent of the people milling around.

Black shit! Ishola's sister carried on . . .

Ishola was out of Oyo in the evening, going towards Oshogbo with her three children. Lijadu would follow the next day and join them in a small village thirty miles out so as to make pursuit fruitless. Lijadu joined her at noon the next day, looking pale and blue and shaken.

What is it with you Lijadu? Why are you so pale? Are you sick?

Silence.

Lijadu what is it?

He sat on the ground and said Mushin has passed away. He passed away about midnight. One of the neighbours found him lying cold in the passage. People say they heard him cry the last time: Ishola, my grandchildren!

Ishola could not move for a few moments. She seemed frozen cold cold cold.

At break of day each morning you will see the women of Oyo with their baskets on their heads. You can see them on the black tarmac going to the market, their bodies twisting at the hip the strong hip. You can see their feet feel their way on the dark tarmac as they ride the dawn, riding into daylight. The figures are slender as twilight. You can see Ishola, too, because she came back, came back to us. She told us that when she heard of the death of her father-in-law she thought, this is not good for my future life with Lijadu I will go back to that cripple . . .

Oyo is an old city in Nigeria. It has some of the most famous markets in the country.

A Point of Identity

It was not until a crisis broke upon Karel Almeida that I began to wonder how he had come to live with us in Corner B location, seven miles out of Pretoria. It was first rumoured that he must be well-to-do. Then people said he *was* rich. And then people went around saying that he had won a huge bet at the race course wherever (no-one cared to know where exactly) it was he had come from. Soon it was said that he was a coloured African. And then again they said, Ach, he's not 'coloured', just one of these blacks with funny names. All these guesses arose from the fact that Karel Almeida was light in complexion, he was large in physique, and he improved the appearance of his three-roomed house within two months or so of his arrival. Also, Almeida laughed a lot, like 'a man who had little to worry him'. But I shouldn't forget to add that he was a bachelor when he arrived, and must have been saving up and living light.

This was little less than ten years ago — I mean when he came to our street and occupied a house next door to mine.

During those years Karel Almeida became 'Karel' to me and my wife and 'uncle Karel' or 'uncle Kale' to the children. We were very fond of each other, Karel and I. We had got to take each other for granted; so it was normal for him, when he was spending his two weeks' leave at home and my wife fell ill, to look after her and cook for her and give her medicines while I was away at school, teaching. He worked in a Jew's motor-mechanic shop in the city, and lived austerely enough.

Karel's whole physical being seemed to be made of laughter. When he was going to laugh, he shook and quivered as if to 'warm up' for a take-off and then the laugh was released like a volley from deep down his large tummy, virtually bullying the listener to join in the 'feast'.

'Hm, just hear how Karel is eating laughter!' my wife would say when the sound issued from Karel's house.

'Me my mudder was African, my farder was Portugalese,' Karel often said in conversation. 'Not, mind you, de Portugalese what come an' fuck aroun' an' have a damn good time an' den dey vamoose off to Lourenco Marques. But de ole man went to LM an' he got sick.' After a pause he burst out, 'An' he die sudden, man, just like you blow a candle out, T.' He always called me 'T' which was an intimate way of referring to me as a schoolteacher.

'Where were you and your mother?'

'In Jo'burg, man. It's now — let me see — one, two, three, *ja*, three years. Died in Sibasa, man, way up nort' Transvaal. My Ma nearly died same day and followed my Pa de day he die. Fainted an' gave us hell to bring her back. She went to LM for de funeral.'

'And now, where's she?'

'Who, my mudder? She's dead — let me see — one, two, two years now. I brought her wit' me to Jo'burg when I was learning mechanics at de same garage what brought me here. Good Jew boss, very good. He got a son at university in Jo'burg. Nice boy too. My Ma didn't like Jo'burg not dis much, so I took her back to Sibasa.'

We often teased each other, Karel and I, he was so full of laughter.

'I can't understand,' I said one day, 'why you cycle to work and back instead of taking a bus. Just look how the rain beats on you and the wind almost freezes you in winter.' He laughed.

'Trouble wit' you kaffirs is you's spoiled.'

'And you Boesmans and Hotnotte are tough, you'll tell me.'

'An' de Coolies, too. See how dey walk from house to house selling small t'ings. Dey's like donkeys, man. Can't catch dem de coolies, man. You and me will never catch dem. It's *dey* who'll always make de money while we Hotnotte an kaffirs sleep or loaf about or stick a knife or plug a bullet into someone or jes work for what we eat an' live in an' laugh at life. Jeeslike man, dey's gone dose Coolies, dey'll beat us at makin' money all de time.'

'But Hotnotte, Boesmans and Kaffirs and coolies are all frying in the same pan, boy, and we're going to sink or swim together, you watch.'

'OK. Kaffir, let's swim.'

'What you got, Boesman?'

'Whisky, gin and lime. But you know, I'm not a Hottentot or a Bushman, I've got European blood straight from de balls no zigzag business about it.'

And, as he served the drinks, his laughter rang pure and clear and solid.

'But serious now, true's God, I've always lived wit' Africans an' never felt watchimball-er-discomfortable or ashamed.' He could never say 'what you call it'. 'Damn it all man if my farder slept wit' mudder an' dey made me dat's dey business. You, T, your great-great-great-grandmudder may have been white or brown woman herself. How can you be sure of any-t'ing? How can any Indian be sure he's hundred percent India? I respec' a man what respec' me no matter his colour.'

He spoke with vehemence and compassion.

Karel took an African woman to live with him as his wife. She was a lovely woman whose background was unknown. She was hardworking and Karel treated her with great affection. She never had much to say, but she was not proud, only shy.

And then the crisis came.

If the whole thing did not begin to set members of a family against one another or individual persons against their communities or vice versa; if it did not drive certain people to the brink of madness and to suicide; if it did not embarrass very dark-skinned people to sit in front of a white tribunal and have to claim 'mixed parentage', then we should have thought that someone had deliberately gone out of his way to have fun, or create it. The white people who governed the country had long been worried about the large numbers of coloured Africans who were fair enough to want to play white, and of Africans who were fair enough to want to try for 'coloured'. They had long been worried about the prospect of one coffee-coloured race, which would shame what they called 'white civilization' and the 'purity' of their European blood. So, maybe, after a sleepless night someone ate his breakfast, read his morning newspapers in between bites, walked about his suburban garden, told his black 'boy' to finish cleaning his car, kissed his wife and children goodbye ('don't expect me for supper, dear'), went to the House of Assembly and began to propel a huge legislative measure through the various formal stages to the President's desk where it would be signed as law. Whatever happened, a board was established to re-classify coloured Africans to decide whether they were to remain on the register as 'coloured' or 'natives'. All people who said that they were 'coloured' had to go to the board for 'tests'.

They were ordered to produce evidence to prove their ancestry (was there a white man or woman in the family tree or not?). The onus was clearly on the subject of the inquiry to prove that he was 'coloured'. Day after day papers were filed: birth certificates; photographs; men, women and children came and lined up before the board. A comb was put into their hair; if it fell out, they must have straight or curly hair and so one condition was fulfilled.

'How tall was your father?' a board member might ask.

'This high,' an exhibit might reply. If he indicated the height by stretching out his arm in a horizontal direction, it was likely that the exhibit was 'coloured'; for Africans generally indicate height by bending the arm at the elbow so that the forearm points in a vertical direction. Another condition fulfilled or found to be an obstruction.

A family woke up one morning wondering if they had been through a dream: some of its members had been declared 'coloured' and others 'native'. But how

was it possible that a whole family could experience
the same dream? Once a 'Native', one had to carry a
pass to permit one to live in an area, to enter another,
to look for work in a town. It would be an in-
defensible criminal offence if one failed to show the
pass to a policeman. Once a 'Native', one's wages had
to be lowered.

'Look, man, T,' Karel said to us one cold evening
after taking a seat in our kitchen. 'I must go to that
board of bastards.'

He took us by surprise. He took a cup of tea from
my wife and stirred it in exaggerated circular movements of his whole arm from the shoulder. He might
have been paddling a canoe, with that arm that
looked like a heavy club. The tea slopped over into
the saucer.

'To the board? But you don't have to tell them
you are a native African?'

Karel looked down.

'What de hell, no.' I looked at my wife, and she
looked at me.

'I told you my farder was Portugalese. Dat makes
me "coloured", *nê*?'

'I know, but . . . ' I did not know what I wanted to
say.

'Look man, T, I — I can't go dress up in de
watchimball er-pass office dere for dis t'ing what you
folks carry. Listen, T, I see youse folks get stopped
by de bloody police day an' night; I see you folks
when de whites at de post office want you to show
your pass before dey give you a parcel or watchimball
— er — registered letter; I see you folks in a line-up on
Sundays morning when police pick you up for not
havin' a pass in your pocket an' dey take you to de
station. Look man, T, one night you don't come

home at de time your wife's waiting to see you, eh?
Now she gets frightened, she t'inks Oh my man may
be locked up. She look for de pass in de house and
dere it is you forgot it. She puts on her shawl an' she
takes de kids next door an' she locks up de house an'
she goes to de police station. Which one? Dere's too
many. She t'inks I must go to de hospital? Maybe
you's hurt or knocked down. But she's sure it must
be some police station. No-one wants to ring de
different stations to fin' out. Hell man she's lost. De
papers tell us all dis plenty times. Sometimes it's de
last time she saw you in de morning when you goes to
work. Maybe you couldn't pay your watchimball — er
— admission of guilt and de police sentences you.
Dere's a lorry waitin' to pick up guys like you wit' no
money for admission or who t'ink you'll talk for
yourself in de magistrate court. A white man takes
you to his farm far way from here to work like slaves.
Maybe you die dere and your wife will never see your
grave, T, never-never.'

I was struck dumb. What argument could one have
against this recital of things one knew only so well?
Hadn't one read these accounts in the press? Hadn't
one seen and known personally families who had
waited for a husband, a son, a cousin, who was never
going to come? Hadn't one read these accounts in the
press and felt something claw inside one's insides and
creep up to the throat and descend to the lower
regions until one seemed untouchably hot all over?

I ventured to say feebly, 'You wouldn't be the
only one, Karel. Isn't one strengthened by the fact
that one is not suffering alone?'

'I ain't no coward, T. What about de wages? My
wages will go down if I simply agree I'm black.
Anudder "coloured" man may push me out of dis

job.'

'But you *are* African, Karel. You as good as said so yourself often. You came to live with us blacks because you felt purity of blood was just lunatic nonsense, didn't you?'

'Look man, T, de word "native" doesn't simply mean one's got black blood or African blood. It's a p'litical word, man. You's a native because you carry a pass, you can't go to watchimball-er-Parliament. You can't vote, you live in dis location. One can be proud of being an African but not a *native.*'

'What does your woman say about this, Karel?'

'Oh you knows she never says not'ing to dis'point me, T.'

'But do you know what she thinks?'

'Can't say, T. Sometime she seems to say Yes, sometime No, but she always say Do what you think is the right thing, Karel.'

My wife and I were sitting up one Saturday night when she said, 'Why does the man keep talking about this like someone who cannot hold hot roasted pumpkin pips in his mouth? Why not go and get the paper to show that he has "coloured" paint on him instead of ringing bells everywhere to tell us he wants to go!'

'No, no, Pulane, you're not being fair. As far as we know, he talks to us only about it.'

'*To us only, ugh!* You should hear people talk about it in the whole street.'

I did not try to ascertain if she meant the whole street, but said instead, 'I think he wants to be sure first he will be doing the right thing.'

'Ach, he's just a coward, finished. Just like all "coloureds". Blacks are nice and good as long as a "coloured" man is not told to become black.'

'Why should anyone want to be black?'

'Isn't it that he wants to show the white people he's "coloured"? Isn't it that he thinks we blacks are nice to live with as long as he doesn't carry a pass as we do and get the same wages as we do? See them. Paul Kruger told them they were like white people and were civilized. Now you go round this corner, "coloured" people have better houses; you turn round that corner, "coloured" people get better money; you go the bioscope the "coloured" people sit at the back and we blacks are put right in front where we can almost kiss the er-what's its name? Ach, they make me feel hot between the thighs these "coloureds"!'

'Would you not want these good things they're getting?'

'Of course! What kind of question is that?'

'But you are not asking to be a "coloured" woman are you?'

'*Sies*, me? Would you like to see me "coloured"?'

'See what I mean! And you seem to want Karel to carry our burdens as a price for liking us and living with us. Who are we to say the "coloured" should not want to keep the good things they have?'

'I just don't want people having it both ways, that's what. They like us as people to laugh with, not to suffer with. We are the laughing cheerful blacks, the ones full of life and entertainment, the ones they run to when they're tired of being "coloureds", Europeans, Indians. As for the Indians, they like their curry and rice and roti and money and mosques and temples too much to pretend they want us for next-door neighbours. I can't blame them because they don't try to bluff anyone. Look how the Indian boys run about with "coloured" girls! They want nothing more than keep their business sites and help us shout from the platform. Ach, they all make me sick these pinks.'

She stood up and took the kettle from the stove with the force it would require if it were glued on. She filled it with water and put it back on the stove, all but throwing it down.

'And you think the Indian folk who join us in protesting are merely bluffing? And the whites, the Indians and "coloureds" whose homes smell of police uniform because of unending raids and who are banned and sent to prison — are they just having a good time, just putting on a performance? Well, I don't know, child of my mother-in-law, but that is a very expensive performance and not so funny.'

These had been times when I wasn't sure myself if I didn't really feel as my wife did.

After a spell of silence she got up to make tea. Meantime I went out to stand on the stoep. For some strange reason, while I looked at the blazing red sky over Iscor steel works five miles away, I thought of Karel's wife. The gentle-looking nurse who never said much any time . . .

Back inside the house, my wife said: 'I wonder how much longer it is going to be for us Africans to keep making allowances and to give way to the next man to turn things round in our head, to do the explaining and to think of others' comfort.'

I looked long into my cup, looking for something clever to say in reply. I could not find it. But I know it had something to do with the African revolution . . .

'I got de identity card at last,' Karel said casually a few months later.

'So!'

'De white trash! Dey wantin' to trap a guy all-a-time, bastards. Man, T, *hulle dink altyd hulle hol 'n mens toe* — dey t'ink dey goin' to drive me into a dead corner, sons of white bitches.' He paused. 'Been waitin' for papers from LM. My late Ma put dem in a box and sent it to LM.' He looked tired and uninterested in his achievement. His voice and posture spelled humiliation to an embarrassing degree — or was it my own embarrassment? Perhaps. I didn't have the courage to ask him to give the details of the examination which must have dragged on for a number of days with a number of breaks.

'So you'll have to leave our location and the law's going to pull you away from your wife.'

'I been t'inking about dat, T. Dey can do all dey want dey'll never do buggerall to me and my woman, true's God. An' I don' take back my identity card. I stay "coloured" and live wit' my woman.'

I thought about my wife's talk about people wanting to have it both ways.

Nor did Karel make any effort to leave Corner B. But we knew that the location's white superintendent would sooner or later be sticking a rough twig between Karel's buttocks to drive him out of the location.

Meantime, Karel's right leg had begun to give him trouble. He was complaining of sleepless nights because of it. He tried to maintain an even tempo in his life, and his laugh was still loud, clear and full. Even so, in the ear of one who knew him as well as I did, it was losing its roundness and developing sharp edges. When the autumn rains came down he complained more and more. He could not pretend any longer that he did not need to limp. He visited

the General Hospital times without number. He was
subjected to radio photography countless times. The
doctors prescribed one thing after another — to drink,
to massage.

'Ach man, T, dese white doctors are playing
around wit' me now. I do everyt'in' dey tell me an' all
dey do is shake dey blerry head wit' sandy brains.
Dey loudmout' when dey tell us dey clever educated
but dey know f-all. *What can I do,* man, I ask dem.
Dey'll kill me wit' dat X-ray one day.'

I felt by proxy the leaping fire that must have been
scorching its way through him to release the tongue
of flame that spoke these words.

One night Karel's wife came to wake me up to
come to him. He wanted to see me, she said. I found
him on top of his blankets, his face wet with
perspiration. His wife was still fully dressed, applying
a hot fomentation.

'Have you ever heard of such a miracle!' his wife
said. Before I could reply she said, 'Karel is talking in
parables I am sure, *hau!* He's telling me he wants to
see a witchdoctor. *Hei,* people, *Modisana!*' She
looked at him as if she was taking out tablets from a
bottle. 'Just ask him.'

'Listen man, T, I'm told some of dese watchimball-
er-witchdoctor guys can do it. If de white man is
beaten maybe black medicine will do it, man.'

'Now you're not going to do such a stupid thing,'
his wife said. I had never heard her speak with such
authority, such a bold face. Here on the question of
sickness and patients, I felt, she was sure of herself.
Looking at me: 'I would rather take him to another
hospital far out of Pretoria, borrow money somewhere, spend all my savings to pay white doctors. Tell
him, you're his friend, tell him, maybe he'll listen to

you.' She stooped to give him his tablets. He turned and lay on his back, with a deep round sigh.

'Listen, T, my woman here t'inks maybe I don' show t'anks for her goodness to me, for her watchimball-er-patience, for her good heart. Hang it man, T, I'm grateful from the bottom of my heart, dat's jes why I want to make it possible for her to rest a bit. She works too hard and has to sit up de whole night a'most lookin' after me.'

'What should a woman be for if she is not there to look after her man?'

'But — but a witchdoctor, man, Karel!' I said.

'You see him as he is,' his wife said. 'His boss has given him a month to stay home — on full pay you hear me? If he rests this leg for a while maybe we'll see which way we are moving. Maybe I can get a few days off to take him out to my people in the Free State. Just to go away from here a bit.'

'I think you should do what this good woman advises, Karel. Forget this witchdoctor madness. Besides, soon as these chaps start mucking around with one's body they're sure to meddle with parts they know nothing about.'

'That is what I keep telling him, you hear.'

I was less convinced about what I was saying than I may have sounded. There were always stories about someone or other who had been cured by a witch-doctor or herbalist after white doctors had failed. The performers of these wonders — as they sounded to be — were invariably said to have come from Vendaland in the farthest recesses of the rain-making queen's territory of the Northern Transvaal. Some time before this a school principal in Corner B had asked a herbalist next to his house to give him a purgative. He had almost immediately become ill and died on his way to hospital. The herbalist had been arrested, but had pleaded that he had advised the teacher to take plenty of water with and after the herb, which thing he must have failed to do. No one had seen him take the herb who could say whether he had followed the instructions or not. Most of us, whether teachers or not, whether townspeople of long standing or not, believed one way or another in ancestral spirits. The same people might at the same time renounce or tolerate the Christian faith or even think their belief in ancestral spirits reinforced. How could anyone be sure? A man like Karel trying to ride a huge wave of pain: what use was there trying to tell him not to seek help outside the hospital? What he said to me the next moment was disarming.

'Listen, T.' He paused as if he had forgotten what he was going to say. 'Listen, de doctor at de hospital says to me yesterday he says I'm sure you got kaffir poison. Kaffir poison, you mean what dey call native poison? I ask. He says, Yes. I say, You can't take out kaffir poison? An' he says No, he says, it's not for white medicine. An' again I says What do you t'ink doctor? An' he shows me he doesn't know.'

'And you think he was telling you what to do without saying so?'

'Yes, dat's not funny. You see for yourself how dese whites queue up at de African watchimball-er-herbalist's place at Selborne.'

'Those are poor whites,' his wife hastened to remark. 'Poor, poor, poor boers or whites from cheap suburbs. What do they know better than that!' 'Dey wouldn't be queuing up every day like dat if he wasn't doing dem any good.' 'Nonsense,' was all I could say. And the cocks started to crow. Just then he dropped off into sleep. I stood up and took his wife's arm to reassure her that I was going to stay on her side.

Once again when Karel could stand up, he walked about. He seemed to have recovered his old cheerful mood again, except for thin lines under his eyes to show that pain had kicked him about and marched through him: with hobnailed boots as it were.

'I feel quite right now,' he said to me. 'Yes, a small slow pain but I t'ink it will go. I must see it goes because I'm sure de boss will not give me more days at de end of de t'irty days. Dey never do dat dese whites. Can't see myself more time in de house if I'm not getting well, and not getting paid neither.'

The note of urgency in his voice told me that he must have something on his mind. What, I wondered.

'I'm goin' to watchimball-to Selborne,' he said another day. 'I'm takin' a bus.'

Two days passed.

'*Hei Wena* — You, our friend had a visitor this morning,' my wife reported.

'What visitor?'

'A man with a bag in his hand. The sort you see witchdoctors carry.'

So, just at the time his wife is at work, I thought.

'Are you going to tell his woman?'

I was irritated at her use of 'you' as if to disengage herself. No, I'd go and tell him a few hard things and I'd not mince words, I told her.

I did, but he only laughed and said I shouldn't be foolish. The man knew the particular ailment he had described to him. Wasn't fussy either about the fee for opening his bag. Yes man, he had thrown the bones and shells on the floor and spoke to them and they told him how things were. Someone had smeared 'some stuff' on his bicycle pedal and it had gone up his leg. Did he say the Jew boss liked him? Yes, very much. Any other black workers at the garage? Two others. Ever had a quarrel with any one of them? Now let's see: No. Was he senior to them? Yes. Some black people have clean hearts, others have black hearts. He could see the way one bone on the fringe was facing. He could hear it talk. He could see one of the garage workers going to an evil doctor to buy black magic.

'It's dere man, T, *die Here weet* — God knows.'

'Do you know a saying in my language that it takes a witch to track down another?' I said.

'I don't care if dis one's a witch. It's my leg gives me worryness. Man T, you can see he can't be lying. His face, his eyes are full of wisdom. He took two days to look for de trouble, *two days.* And he talks to me nice, T, takes de trouble, not like dose white watchimball — bastards at de hospital!'

I left him after his wife had entered.

The next day, instead of taking my sandwiches and tea in the staff-room, I cycled home in order to see how Karel was. My mind was full of ugly forebodings . . . My wife told me that she had taken him lunch as usual but found the 'visitor' and so did not stay. Karel did not look worse than the previous day.

When I entered, the 'visitor' was not there. But Karel was lying on the bed, his leg stretched out and resting on a tiny bench. Under the bench was a rag, saturated with blood. 'What have you done, Karel!' I exclaimed.

'I feel all right, T. De leg will be all right from now. The man dug a hole in the ankle for the poison to come out. Ah!' He released a long heavy sigh. He held his hip with his still-powerful hand, and let it slide down his side, thigh and leg, like one pressing something out of a tube. At the same time he screwed up his face to show how much energy he was putting into the act.

'Ah, T,' came the long long sigh again, 'I can feel de watchimball — de pain moving out of the hole there. The blood is carrying it out. Oh, shit!' After a pause, he said, 'A black man like you T, can go a long way. A black man has people around him to give him strength. I haven't.'

The facial muscles relaxed and his arm hung limp at his side. I looked at the ankle more carefully this time, as much as I could dare. The sight of the blood oozing out like that from the inside part of the ankle, and the soaking wet rag on the floor shocked me out of my stupor and confusion. I looked around for any cloth, found it and bandaged the ankle. Without a word, I ran out to my house. I scribbled a note to my headmaster and asked my wife to go and watch over Karel while I went for a doctor a few streets up. He was out for home visiting together with his nurse. I was frantic. Move him to hospital twelve miles away? The white hospital four miles away would not touch him. What about transport? Go to the location superintendent to ring the hospital? I gave up. I left a note for the doctor. I went back to wait.

Death came and took him away from us.

While I was helping to clear things up in the house, several days later when Karel's wife was permitted by custom to re-organize things in the house, she said to me: 'I believe Karel once told you about his identity card?' 'Yes.' She held it in her hand. 'I don't know if I should keep it.'

My thinking machine seemed to have come to a dead stop and I couldn't utter a word.

'Ach, what use is it?' she said.

'Can I see it please?'

Below his picture appeared many other bits of information:

NAME: KAREL BENITO ALMEIDA

RACE: COLOURED

I gave it back. She tore it into bits.

'Did he tell you about this letter?' She handed it over to me.

It was a letter from the location's white superintendent telling Karel that he would have to leave house No 35 Mathole Street where he was known to live, and was forbidden from occupying any other house in Corner B as he was registered 'coloured' and should not be in a 'Bantu location'.

She took the letter and tore it to bits.

'Soon I know I must leave this house.'

'Why? You can tell the superintendent that you are his widow. I know widows are always ejected soon as their men are under the ground. We can help you fight it out.' But I knew this was useless heroic talk: the law of the jungle always wins in the end. But that is another story. And in any case, 'I was not married to Karel by law,' the good woman said.

Grieg on a Stolen Piano

Those were the days of terror when, at the age of 15, he ran away from home and made his way towards Pietersburg town. Driven by hunger and loneliness and fear he took up employment on an Afrikaner's farm at ten shillings a month plus salted mealie-meal porridge and an occasional piece of meat. There were the long scorching hours when a posse of horsemen looked for him and three other labourers while they were trying to escape. The next morning at dawn the white men caught up with them.

Those were the savage days when the whole white family came and sat on the stoep to watch, for their own amusement, African labourers put under the whip. Whack! Whack! Whack! And while the leather whip was still in the air for the fourth stroke on the buttocks, he yelled, *ma-oeeee!* As the arm came down, he flew up from the crude bench he was lying on, and, in a manner that he could never explain afterwards, hooked the white foreman's arm with his two, so that for a few seconds he dangled a few feet from the ground. Amid peals of laughter from the small pavilion, the foreman shook him off as a man does a disgusting insect that creeps on his arm.

Those were the days when, in a solo flight again towards Pietersburg, terror clawed at his heart as he travelled through thick bush. He remembered the stories he had so often listened to at the communal fire-place; tales of huge snakes that chased a man on the ground or leapt from tree to tree; tales of the giant snake that came to the river at night to drink, breaking trees in its path and before which helpless people lay flat on their stomachs wherever they might be at the time; none dared to move as the snake mercifully lifted its body above them, bent over, drank water and then, mercifully again, turned over backwards, belly facing upwards, rolling away from the people; stories that explained many mysteries, like the reason why the owl and the bat moved in the dark. Always the theme was that of man, helpless as he himself was in the bush or on a tree or in a rock cave on a hill, who was unable to ward off danger, to escape a terrible power that was everywhere around him. Something seemed to be stalking him all the time, waiting for the proper moment to pounce upon him.

But he walked on, begged and stole food and got lifts on lorries, until he reached Thswane — Pretoria.

There was the brief time in 'the kitchens', as houses of white people are called where one does domestic work, as if the white suburbs were simply a collection of kitchens. There were the brutal Sundays when he joined the Pietersburg youth, then working in the kitchens, on their wild march to the open ground just outside Bantule location for a sport of bare fisticuffs. They marched in white shorts on broad slabs of feet in tennis shoes and vaseline-smeared legs: now crouching, now straightening up, now wielding their fists wrapped in white handkerchiefs. One handkerchief dangled out of a trouser pocket, just for show. The brutal fisticuffs, mouths flushed with blood; then the white mounted police who herded them back to the kitchens; the stampede of horses' hooves as the police chased after them, for fun . . .

Those were the days when chance lifted him like a crane out of the kitchens and out of the boxing arena, and deposited him in Silvertown location. This was when his aunt, having been alerted by her brother, had tracked him down.

There was regular schooling again. At twenty he began teacher-training at Kilnerton Institution near-by. There were the teaching days, during which he studied privately for a junior secondary school certificate.

Those were the days, when, as the first black man in the province to write an examination for this certificate, he timidly entered a government office for the first paper. The whites stared at him until he had disappeared into the room where he would write in isolation. And those were the days when a black man had to take off his hat as soon as he saw a white man approach, when the black man had to keep clear of street pavements.

Then the return home — the first time in seven years — as a hero, a teacher. The parents bubbled over with pride. Then the feast . . .

It was one of those hot subtropical nights when Pretoria seems to lie in its valley, battered to insensibility by the day's heat, the night when a great friend of his was tarred and feathered by white students of the local university at Church Square:

Mr Lambeth, a British musician who had come to teach at Kilnerton where he discovered this black young man's musical talent. He had given his time free to teach him the piano. Many were the afternoons, the nights, the weekends that followed of intensive, untiring work at the instrument. What else had Mr Lambeth done wrong, he asked himself several times after the incident. The Englishman had many friends among African teachers whom he visited in their locations; he adjudicated at their music competitions.

This black young man was my uncle. He was actually a cousin of my late father's. So, according to custom, my father had referred to him as 'my brother'. As my father had no blood brothers, I was glad to avail myself of an uncle. When my father died, he charged my uncle with the responsibility of 'helping me to become a man'. It meant that I had someone nearby who would give me advice on a number of things concerned with the problem of growing up. My mother had died shortly afterwards. Uncle has seven children, all but one of whom are earning their living independently. The last-born is still in school.

Uncle is black as a train engine; so black that his face often gives the illusion of being bluish. His gums are a deep red which blazes forth when he smiles, overwhelming the dull rusty colour of his teeth. He is tall and walks upright. His head is always close-shaven, because, at sixty, he thinks he is prematurely greying, although his hair began to show grey at thirty. He keeps his head completely bald because he does not want a single grey hair to show.

His blackness has often led him into big-big trouble with the whites, as he often tells us.

'Hei! Jy!'

Uncle walks straight on, pretending not to see the bunch of them leaning against a fence. He is with a friend, a classmate.

'Hei! Jy! die pikswart een, die bobbejaan!' — the pitch-black one, the baboon.

One of them comes towards the two and pushes his way between them, standing in front. They stop dead.

A juvenile guffaw behind him sends a shiver through Uncle. He breaks through his timidity and lunges at the white boy. He pommels him. In Pietersburg boxing style he sends the body down with a knee that gets him on a strategic place on the jaw. The others are soon upon them. The Africans take to their heels . . .

A new white clerk is busy arranging postal orders and recording them. The queue stretches out, out of the post office building. The people are making a number of clicking noises to indicate their impatience. They crane their necks or step out of the queue in order to see what is happening at the counter.

Uncle is at the head of the queue.

'Excuse me,' he ventures, 'playtime will soon be over and my class will be waiting for me, can you serve us, please?'

The clerk raises his head.

'Look here,' he says aggressively, 'I'm not only here to serve kaffirs, I'm here to work!'

Uncle looks at him steadily. The clerk goes back to his postal orders. After about fifteen minutes he leaves them. He goes to a cupboard and all the eyes in the queue follow each movement of his. When he comes back to the counter, he looks at the man at the head of the queue, who in turn fixes his stare on him.

The white man seems to recoil at the sight of Uncle's face. Then, as if to fall back on the last mode of defence, he shouts 'What are you? What are you? — just a black kaffir, a kaffir monkey, black as tar. Now any more from you and I'll bloody well refuse to serve the whole bloody lot of you. Teacher — teacher, teacher *te hel!*'

Irritation and impatience can be heard to hiss and sigh down the queue.

Uncle realizes he's being driven into a corner and wonders if he can contain the situation. Something tells him it is beyond him. The supervisor of post comes in just then, evidently called in by his junior's shout.

'Ja?' he asks, *'wat is dit?'*

'Your clerk has been insulting me — calling me a Kaffir monkey.'

The clerk opens his mouth to speak, but his superior leads him round a cubicle. After a few moments, the clerk comes back, ready to serve but sulky, and mute.

Uncle says that throughout the white clerk seemed to feel insulted at the sudden confrontation of such articulate human blackness as thrust itself forward through the wire mesh of the counter.

This time, Uncle had the satisfaction of causing the removal of the white clerk after a colleague, who had been an eye witness of the incident in the post office, had obtained support from fellow-teachers at Silverton to petition a higher postal authority against the clerk.

'Can you see that happening today?' he asked. 'No, man, I'd have been fired at once on a mere allegation out of the clerk's important mouth.'

Years later, Uncle was promoted to the post of junior inspector of African schools (the white man always senior). He went to live in the Western Transvaal. This is where his wife died while giving birth. He really hit the bottom of depression after this. The affection he had for his wife found a perverse expression in drink and he took to his music with a deeper and savage passion which, as he puts it, was a kind of hot fomentation to help burst the boil of grief inside him. He kept his children with him, though. Each one had the opportunity to go to an institution of higher education. Here he was lucky. For although all of them were mediocre, they used what they had profitably and efficiently. One did a degree in science; another played the saxophone in a band; another was a teacher and 'pop singer'; another became a librarian for an institute of research into race relations; one daughter went in for nursing, and a son and a daughter were still in secondary school.

There were nights of sheer terror when their father failed to return home, and they knew he must be in some drinking orgy somewhere. Then they got to know that he was doing illicit diamond-buying. As he visited schools in his circuit, he sold or bought small stones. But he was always skating near the edge. Once he had the bitter experience of discovering that he had bought a few fakes for £50 from an African agent.

Then there was the day he says he'll never forget as long as he lives. The CID, after crossing his path several times and picking up and losing trails, finally came to the converging point — Uncle. They found him in a train from Johannesburg to Kimberley. They took him to the luggage van and questioned him. Nothing was found on him, and he wouldn't talk.

When eventually they realized they might have a corpse on their hands, they put him out on a station platform, battered, bleeding and dazed. His suitcase was thrown in his direction.

Uncle was transferred to Johannesburg, but not without incident. A white educational officer wanted him to carry his typewriter — a heavy table model — to his car outside. Uncle told him he wouldn't. He had before refused to wash the official's car when asked to do so. As the educational authorities had a high opinion of his work after serving several years in the department, they engineered a transfer for him. If you ask him how he managed to keep his post, he will tell you, 'I made more or less sure I didn't slip up that side, and besides whites don't like a correct black man, because they are so corrupt themselves.'

Each time after some verbal tiff with a white man, Uncle says, he felt his extra blackness must have been regarded as an insult by those who found themselves in the shadow it seemed to cast around him.

His arrival in Johannesburg was like surfacing. He went slow on his drink, and even became a lay preacher in the Methodist Church at Orlando. But he started to go to the races, and threw himself into this kind of gambling with such passion that he resigned as preacher.

'I can't keep up the lies,' he said. 'There are people who can mix religion with gambling and the other things, but I can't. And gamble I must. As Christ never explained what a black man should do in order to earn a decent living in this country, we can only follow our instincts. And if I cannot understand the connection, it is not right for me to stand in the pulpit and pretend to know the answer.'

The 'other things' were illicit diamond dealing and

trading as a travelling salesman, buying and selling soft goods, mostly stolen by some African gang or other that operated in the city. There were also workers who systematically stole articles from their employers' shops and sold them to suburban domestic servants and location customers. While he was visiting schools, he would call this man and that man round the corner or into some private room to do business.

Uncle married again. He was now living with three of his children, two of whom were still in secondary school. A cloud descended upon his life again. His wife was an unpleasant, sour woman. But Uncle woke up to it too late. She sat on the stoep like a dumpling and said little beyond smiling briefly a word of greeting and giving concise answers to questions. The children could not quarrel with her, because she said little that could offend anyone. But her antheap appearance was most irritating, because she invited no-one's co-operation and gave none beyond fulfilling the routine duties of a wife. She did not seem to like mothering anyone.

Once she succeeded, perhaps in all innocence, in raising a furore in the house.

'You must find out more about the choir practice your daughter keeps going to every week,' she says to Uncle in the presence of the other children. They had stopped calling her 'Ma' because she insisted on referring to them as 'your daughter' or 'your son' when she talked to their father about them.

'It's choir practice,' Uncle said brusquely.

'*Wai-i-i!* I know much about choir practices, me. A man's daughter can go to them without stopping and one-two-three the next time you look at her she has a big choir practice in her stomach.'

The girl ran into her bedroom, crying. Soon tongues were let loose upon her. But she continued to sit like an antheap, her large body seeming to spread wider and wider like an overgrown pumpkin. Her attitude seemed to suggest much Uncle would have liked to know. What *was* she hiding?

'What do you do with such a woman?' Uncle sighed when he told me about the incident.

He was prepared to go through with the 'companionship', to live with her to the end of his days. 'I promised I'd do so in church,' he remarked. 'And I was in my full senses, no-one forced me into the thing.'

Another time he threatened, 'One day I'll get so angry, neph', I'll send her away to her people. And at her station I'll put her on a wheelbarrow like a sack of mealies and wheel her right into her people's house if I've to bind her with a rope.'

I knew he was never going to do it.

Uncle could only take dramatic decisions which were not going to leave him any need to exercise responsibility either to revoke them or fall back on them. He made decisions as a man makes a gamble: once made, you won or lost, and the matter rested there. It was the same with his second marriage, I think. He met the woman during a church conference when he was by chance accommodated in her house in Randfontein together with two other delegates, according to the arrangements of the local branch. His wife had been dead twelve years. He had decided that his children were big enough not to look so helpless if a second marriage soured the home atmosphere by any chance. His personal Christian belief would not permit him to get out of a marriage contract. This was the kind of responsibility he would want to avoid. If there was a likely chance that he might have to decide to revoke a step later, he did not take it.

There was in Uncle a synthesis of the traditional and the westernised African. At various periods in his life he felt that ill-luck was stalking him, because misfortune seemed to pour down on him in torrents, particularly in money matters, family relations, and relations with white educational authorities. At times like these, Uncle went and bought a goat, slaughtered it, and called relations to come and eat the meat and mealie-meal porridge with their bare hands, sitting on the floor. He then buried the bones in the yard. At such times his mind searched the mystery of fate, groping in some imagined world where the spirits of his ancestors and that of his dead wife must be living, for a point of contact, for a line of communion.

After the feast, he felt peace settle inside him and fill his whole being until it seemed to ooze from the pores of his body as the tensions in him thawed . . . Then he would face the world with renewed courage or with the reinforced secure knowledge that he was at peace with his relations, without whom he considered he would be a nonentity, a withered twig that has broken off from its tree.

Twice when I was ill, Uncle called in an African medical doctor. But when my migraine began and often seemed to hurl me into the den of a savage beast, he called in an African herbalist and witch-doctor. The man said he could divine from his bones that I had once — it didn't matter when or where — inhaled fumes that had been meant to drive me insane, prepared by an enemy. So he in turn burned a few sticks of a herb and made me inhale the smoke. It shot up my nasal cavity, hit the back of my skull, seeming to scrape or burn its path from the forehead to the nape of my neck. Each time, after repeated refusals to be seen by a medicine man, my resistance broke down. I felt temporary relief each time.

So he was going to keep his wife, rain or shine. When her behaviour or her sullenness depressed him, he went back to his whisky. Then he played excerpts from Grieg's piano concerto or a Chopin nocturne, or his own arrangements of Mohapeloa's *Chuchu-makhala* (the train) or *Leba* (the dove) and others, vocalizing passages the while with his deep voice. He loved to evoke from his instrument the sound of the train's siren *Oi-oi-i-i* while he puffed *chu-chu, chu-chu.*

'If she knew this piano was lifted out of a shop,' he thought aloud often, 'this dumpling would just let off steam about the fact, simply to annoy me, to make me feel I'm a failure because she knows I'm not a failure and she wants to eat me up and swallow me up raw the way she did her first husband.'

He had lately disposed of his twenty-year-old piano.

The keyboard felt the impact of these passionate moments and resounded plaintively and savagely. Self-pity, defiance, despising, endurance, all these and others, played musical chairs in his being.

'Look, neph,' Uncle said one day when he was his cheerful, exuberant self again, 'look, here's an advertisement of an African beauty contest in *Afric.*'

'Oh, there is such a rash of beauty contests these days we're all sick of them. It's the racket in every big town these days. Haven't they learned that a woman is as beautiful as your eyes make her?'

'You're just too educated, that's all. You know nothing, my boy, wait till I tell you.'

'Is it a new money-catching thing again? Don't tell me you're going to run a gambling game around the winning number.'

Uncle and beauty queens simply did not dovetail in my mind. What was behind that volume of blackness that frightened so many whites? I was curious to know.

'Better than that, neph'. If you want to co-operate.'

'In what?'

'Now look at the prizes: £500, £250, £150 and consolation prizes. One of these can be ours.'

'But this is a beauty contest, not a muscle show.'

'Don't be so stupid. Now, here. I know a lovely girl we can enter for this contest.'

I felt my curiosity petering out.

'I go and fetch the girl — she's a friend's daughter living in the Western Transvaal, in a village. Just the right kind of body, face, but she needs to be brought up to market standard. The contest is nine months away still, and we've time.'

'But —'

'Now listen. You put in £25, me the same. We can then keep the girl in my house — no, your aunt will curdle again — now let me think — Yes, in my friend Tau's house; his wife has a beautiful heart. The money will go to feeding her and paying for her lessons at Joe's gym. Your job will be to take her out, teach her how to smile when she's introduced; how to sit — not like an Afrikaner cow. You've got to cultivate in her a sense of public attention. Leave the body work to Joe. If she wins, we give her £100, and split £400.'

Joe was one of those people who knows just when to come in for profit. He sets up his gym in a hired hall with the express aim of putting candidates through 'body work'.

For my part, I simply did not like the idea at all. Beauty on a platform: beauty advertized, beauty mixed up with money; that is how the thing seemed to me, a person with the simple tastes of a lawyer's clerk. To what extent Uncle had assimilated jazzy urban habits, I couldn't tell.

'Thought about it yet, neph'? We can't wait too long, you know.'

'Yes, Unc', but I just don't see the point of it. Why don't we leave beauty queens to the — er — experts?' I actually meant something much lower than experts. 'Like Joe, for instance.'

'Joe's just a spiv,' Uncle replied. 'He just loves to rub shoulders with top dogs, that's all. We are investing.'

'But I've only £30 in the post office savings; if I take out $25, I shall be almost completely out.'

'A black man never starves if he lives among his people, unless there is famine. If the worst comes to the worst, you would have to be content with simply having food, a roof over your head, and clothing.'

'That's rural thinking. The extra things a man wants in the city I can't afford.'

'Two hundred pounds can give you the extras.'

I paused to think.

'No, Unc', gambling is for the rich, for those who can afford to lose, not for people like us.'

'You think I'm rich? Don't be silly, you mean to say all those hunch-backed, dried-up, yellow-coloured whites you see at the races and betting booths are rich?'

I relented after a good deal of badgering. Who knows, I thought, we may just win. What couldn't I do with £200 if it came to me!

What a girl!

Her face was well shaped all right: every feature of it was in place, although she had a dry mouth and an unpleasant complexion. She could not have been well in the Western Transvaal. Her bones stuck out at the elbows, and her buttocks needed filling out.

'What is your name?' I asked her.

'Tryphina.' I almost giggled, thinking: What names some people have!

'That name won't do, Unc',' I said to him at the house, affecting a touch of showmanship. 'I can't imagine the name coming out of the mouth of the MC when he calls it out.'

'Call her "try" or "Tryph", ' he said indifferently.

'No, they sound like syllables in a kindergarten reading class. Just as bad as "Jenina" or "Judida" or "Hermina" or "Stephina".'

'Let's use her Sesotho name; she should have one I'm sure.'

'Torofina,' she said.

'No, not the school name spoken in Sesotho, I mean your real Sotho name. You see, in things like a beauty competition, people like an easy name that is smooth on the tongue (I meant *sweet to the ear*). They may even fail you for having a difficult name.'

Didn't I loathe *Afric's* cheap slick, noisy journalism.

'Oh, Kefahliloe,' she said sweetly, which means 'something has got into my eye.' 'That is what they call me at home.'

'Nice,' I commented, meaning nothing of the sort. 'But you don't have a shorter Sesotho name?'

'No.' She was still all innocence and patience.

'Well — er — maybe you can — er — think of an

English name. Just for the contest, you see, and for
the newspapers and magazines. Your picture is going
to appear in all the papers. We'll call you Kefahliloe —
a person's name is her name, and there's nothing
wrong in it. Do not hurry, you can tell us the name
you've chosen later. Is it all right?' She nodded.
Things never seemed all wrong with her. Sometimes
there was something pathetic about her pliability,
sometimes irritating.

The next day she gave it to us, with a take-it-or-
leave-it tone: Mary-Jane.

The first three months showed a slight improvement.
Her weight was going up, her paleness was disappearing, the lips moistening and softening, her
small eyes taking on a new liveliness and self-
confidence. Joe was doing the body work efficiently.
I felt then, and Uncle agreed, like one who had
known it all along, that there was something latent in
the girl which we were going to draw out in the next
few months.

She had finished her primary schooling and done
part of secondary school, so she was all right on that
side.

I took her to the bioscope on certain Saturdays,
especially musicals, which appealed to her more than
straight drama or bang-bang movies. I took her to
Dorkay House in Eloff Street where African
musicians go each Saturday for jazz improvisations.
There we found other boys and girls listening eagerly,
ripples of excitement visibly travelling through the
audience as now and again they whistled and clapped
hands. The girls were the type called in township
slang 'rubbernecks', the ostentatiously jazz type. We
found the same type at parties.

Mary-Jane was drinking it all in, I noticed.

I invited her to my room to listen to my collection of jazz records. She took in small doses at a time, and seemed to digest it and her bodily movements were taking on a city rhythm.

Uncle and I shared entertainment expenses equally. We went for cheap but good entertainment.

After six months, Uncle and I knew we were going to deliver a presentable article of good healthy flesh, comportment, and luscious charm. Charm? Strange. Through all this I did not notice the transformation that was taking place in this direction. She was close on twenty-one, and at the end of the next six months, I was struck by the charm that was creeping out of her, seeming to wait for a time, far off, when it would burst into blossom. She was filling out, but her weight was in no danger of overshooting the mark. Her tongue was loosening up.

I was becoming aware of myself. I felt a twinge of guilt at treating her like an article that should be ready against a deadline. Before I could realize fully what was happening, the storm had set in. The thing was too delicate; I would have to go about it carefully. Particularly so because I had sensed that she was innocent and untutored in a rustic manner about things like love. And one didn't want the bird to take fright because one had dived into the bush instead of carefully burrowing in. Besides, I am a timid fellow, not unlike my uncle in other things.

Uncle had expensive photographs taken of Mary-Jane for the press. Publicity blazed across the African newspapers, and the air was thick with talk about *Afric's* beauty contest at which Miss Johannesburg would be selected. 'Who was going to be the 500-pound consignment of beauty dynamite?' the journal screamed . . .

I heard a snatch of conversation in the train one morning amid the continuous din of talking voices, peals of laughter and door-slamming.

'Hey man, see dat girl's picture in *Afric?*'

'Which?'

'De one called Mary-Jen — er — Tumelo?'

'Ja-man, Jesus, she's reely top, eh!'

'God, de body, hmm, de curves, de waist, dis t'ings!' (indicating the area of the breasts).

'Ach man, dat's number one true's God jealous down.'

I warmed up towards the boys and wished they could continue.

'I've seen the three judges,' Uncle said.

'The judges? But *Afric* hasn't published the names!'

'They don't *do* such things, you backward boy.'

'How did you know them?'

'I've my contacts.'

'But we don't do such things, Uncle!' I gasped.

'What things?'

'Talking to judges about a competition in which you have vested interests.'

'Don't talk so pompously. You're talking English. Let's talk Sesotho. Now all I did is I took photographs of Mary-Jane to each one at his house, paid my respects with a bottle of whisky and asked them if they didn't think she's a beautiful girl. What's wrong with just talking?'

'What did they think?'

'What are you talking, neph'! Each one almost jumped out of his pants with excitement.'

I wanted badly to laugh, but wanted also to show

him that I disapproved.

'I didn't suggest anything to them. I just said she is my niece and I was proud to see her entering the contest. They swore they hadn't seen such beauty so well photographed among all the pictures they had seen in the papers. We're near the winning post, neph', I can see the other side of September the fifteenth already — it's bright. Those judges caught my hint.'

I continued to sit with my eyes fixed on the floor, wondering whether I should feel happy or alarmed.

'By the way, neph', do you realize you have got yourself a wife, home-grown and fresh? Anything going on between you two?'

'What do you mean?' I asked without wanting an answer. His eyes told me he wasn't impressed by my affectation. He waited for me to crawl out of it.

'I haven't thought of it,' I lied. After a pause, 'Was this also on your mind when you thought of her as a beauty queen, Uncle?'

'Yes, neph'. I got to liking her very much while I visited her people during my inspection trips. I was sad to think that such a bright pretty girl would merely become another villager's wife and join the rest who are scratching the soil like chickens for what food there still remains in those desolate places. Her father and me are like twin brothers, we were at school together.'

'But the contest? Surely you could obtain a husband for her without it? And you're not sure she'll win either.'

He was silent.

'Nor are we sure she'll like me for a husband.'

'Her father knows my plans. He has told her since she came here.'

'But the contest, why that?'

Silence.

'It's too difficult to explain. All I ask you is to trust me enough to know that I'm not simply playing a game with Mary-Jane for my own amusement.'

During the next few days vanity blew me up. I abstracted the whole sequence of events from their setting and the characters who acted them out. Gradually I built up a picture of myself as someone who needs to be independent and around whom a hedge was being set up, a victim of a plot. I regarded myself as a sophisticate who couldn't willingly let others choose a sweetheart or wife for me. But in fact I sensed that the reason for my resentment was that I was actually in love with Mary-Jane but could not face the prospect of living with someone I had presumed to raise to a level of sophistication for reasons of money. I had often been moved by films in which the hero eventually married the less-privileged, artless and modest girls rather than the articulate, urbanised girl who goes out to get her man. Now I had the opportunity of doing the same thing, and I couldn't. In either case, I realize now, one saw a different version of male vanity at work.

Another disturbing element was my uncle's motive for doing what he did by throwing Mary-Jane into a beauty contest when he could arrive at his other objective without going into all the trouble. Although he declined to say it, I think it was his gambling urge that pushed him to it. I wondered what Mary-Jane herself thought about all this: the manner in which she was simply brought to the city and put through a machine to prepare her for a beauty competition, probably without her opinion being asked. Did she perhaps take it that this was how townspeople did things, or one of the things country people were bound to do when they came to the city? I still wonder.

Mary-Jane had to enter the competition, in spite of our vanities. She looked forward to it with zest and a certain vivacity which one would not have guessed she was capable of about nine months before. Yes, she was charming, too. How I wished I had found her like this or had arrived at it through someone else's efforts and planning!

Uncle himself infected me with his high spirits. We decided to have an Indian dinner at the Crescent, after the event.

That night came.

The lights went on full beam, washing out every bit of shade from every corner of the hall. The Jazz Dazzlers struck up 'September in the Rain'. Masses of faces in the packed hall looked up towards the rostrum. The music stopped. The MC's voice cut through the noise in the hall and the people held their breaths, unfinished words and sentences trailing off in a sigh.

It came to me with a metallic mockery — the announcement that *Afric* had decided that this was going to be a you-pick-the-winner show. The queen and the other two prize winners would be chosen by popular vote. There was hilarious applause and whistling from the crowd of what must have been about two thousand people. The MC explained that as the people filed out of the hall after the contest, each person would, in the presence of supervisors at the door, drop two tickets into a box fixed at every one of the four exits. One ticket would bear the numbers of the winners of the three prizes in evening dress, and the other card numbers of the winners in beach attire. The categories were indicated on the cards. Then pencils were distributed, while the band played.

I looked at Uncle next to me. I could see he was furious. He kept saying, 'Stupid! Hoodlums! Cheats! Burn the bloody *Afric!* Nothing ever goes right in things organized by the Press. You take my word for it, neph'. Ah!'

'Anything happens in beauty competitions,' I said, for lack of a stronger remark to match my sagging mood.

'Anyway, neph',' Uncle said, his face cheering up, 'two thousand people looking with two eyes each must be better than three men looking with two eyes each, with the possibility of a squint in one of them.'

This really tickled me, in spite of myself. It gave me hope: how could one be sure that all three judges knew a lovely bust from the back of a bus or a bag of mealies? We could at least enjoy our Indian dinner and leave the rest in the hands of fate.

What use would it be to describe Mary-Jane's superb performance?

We had couples — friends — with us at dinner. Mary-Jane was most relaxed. Her ingenuous abandon and air of self-assurance went to my head. The dinner proved worth waiting for. That went to my stomach and made me feel what a glorious thing it is to have a healthy receptacle for such exquisite food.

During our 12-mile trip by car to Orlando, I felt the warm plush body of Mary-Jane press against me slightly, and I was glad to have things in contact like that. She, in turn, seemed to respond to something of what was radiating from me.

'Are you worried about the results?' I ventured to ask, merely for the sake of saying something to relieve the drowsy full-bellied silence in the car.

'No,' she replied warmly. 'Not a bit. But I am glad it's all over.'

We lost.

Mary-Jane wasn't in the least worried. Uncle regarded it simply as a match that was lost and couldn't be replayed. For my part, I suspected that I had often heard a faint whisper within me telling me that I should be better off if we lost. So I did not know what I ought to feel.

On a Sunday I went to Uncle's house for a casual visit. I found his wife in one of her sour moods. She greeted me with the impatience of one who waves off a fly that hovers over the face and hinders conversation. She was actually talking alone, in a querulous mood. Her right elbow was resting on her huge breast and in the cup of the left hand, the right hand stroking her cheek and nose.

I passed hastily on to the room where Uncle played and sang an excerpt from Grieg's piano concerto. He saw me as I went to seat myself, but continued to play. At the end of a passage he said, casually, 'She is gone,' and continued playing. I shrugged my shoulders, thinking, 'That's beyond me.'

'She left me a note,' he said. 'Did you receive one?'

His eyes told me that he had just visited his whisky cupboard. I realized that he wasn't talking about his wife.

'Who? Are you talking about Mary-Jane?'

He nodded. 'Who do you think I mean — Vasco da Gama's daughter-in-law?' Then he shouted, '*Ja*. Gone. With Joe!'

He went back to some crescendo passages of Grieg, picking them up and dropping them in turn. Then he suddenly stopped and came to sit by me.

'How's everybody in the house?' I asked.

'Still well. Except your aunt. That stupid native boy who sold me this piano comes here and finds your aunt and tells her this is a stolen piano. Just showing off, the clever fool. *Setlatla sa mafelelo* — fool of the first order. His mother never taught him not to confide everything in woman. Kind of lesson you suck from your mother's breast. The native! Now your aunt thinks all the house money goes out for the piano. Nothing can convince her that I'm paying £30 only, and in bits, too. So, you see, she's staging one of her boycotts.'

Uncle did not even pretend to lower his voice. Has it gone this far — no bother about what she thinks? I asked myself. No, he did care. He was too sensitive not to care. Always, when he told me about her, he spoke with a sense of hurt. Not such as a henpecked husband displays: Uncle had tremendous inner resources and plenty of diversions and could not buckle up under his wife's policy of non-collaboration, the way a henpecked man would do. This 'speaking up' was just a bit of defiance.

'She worries about a stolen piano,' Uncle continued, lying back on the divan, his eyes looking at the ceiling, his thumb playing up and down under his braces. 'She forgets she sleeps between stolen sheets; every bit of cutlery that goes into her mouth was stolen by the boys from whom I bought it; her blouses are stolen goods, her stockings.' And then, looking at me he said, 'Don't we steal from each other, lie to each other every day and know it, us and the whites?'

I said, *'Ja'* and looked at my tie and shoes. But I considered this superfluous explanation.

'You know, neph',' he continued in rambling fashion. 'A few days ago I had a sickening experience involving a school I've been inspecting. A colleague of mine — let's call him JM — has been visiting the school for oral tests. At no time when his white superior calls him or asks him a question does JM fail to say 'Yes, baas', or 'No, baas', or 'I'll get it for you, baas.' Now during the lunch break, some of the staff say to him in the staffroom they feel disgraced when a black man like him says 'baas, baas' to the white man. They say they hope he'll stop it — just a nice brotherly talk, you see. Guess what JM goes and does? He goes and tells his white superior that the staff members of such-and-such a school don't want him to call him 'baas'! Guess what the white man does? He comes and complains to me about the bad conduct of those teachers. Now I ask you, what chance do you or I stand against idiots like these two who have so much power? We don't all have the liver to join the Congress Movement. So we keep stealing from the white man and lying to him and he does the same. This way we can still feel some pride.'

As I rose to go, I said, 'So Mary-Jane's gone off with Joe, eh!' as though her image had not been hovering over me all the time since Uncle had announced her 'flight'.

'Yes, because I've a stupid timid nephew. Are you going to wait till horns grow on your head before you marry?'

I laughed.

'Any country girl who starts off with Joe has made a real start in town living, neph!'

As I went out, the woman in the lounge was saying; 'Kiriki, Kiriki — who do they say he is? — Kiriki with the stolen piano. Me, I cannot eat Kiriki, I

want money for food. He can take that Kirikinyana
and Mohapeloanyana of his, put them in the lavatory
bucket.'

By saying 'He can take . . . ', she clearly wanted me
to listen. The use of the diminutive form for the
names of the musicians was meant for his ears.

'What do you do with your aunt, neph', if she does
not understand Grieg and cannot like Mohapeloa?'

If you had pricked me with a pin as I was going
out, I should have punctured, letting out a loud bawl
of laughter which I could hardly keep back in my
stomach.

In Corner B

How can boys just stick a knife into someone's man like that? Talita mused. Leap out of the dark and start beating up a man and then drive a knife into him. What do the parents of such boys think of them? What does it matter now? I'm sitting in this room weeping till my heart wants to burst . . .

Talita's man was at the government mortuary, and she sat waiting, waiting and thinking in her house. A number of stab wounds had done the job, but it wasn't till he had lain in hospital for a few hours that the system caved in and he turned his back on his people, as they say. This was a Thursday. But if one dies in the middle of the week, the customary thing is to wait for a week and be buried at the first weekend after the seven days. A burial must be on a weekend to give as many people as possible an opportunity to attend it. At least a week must be allowed for the next-of-kin to come from the farthest parts of the country.

There are a number of things city folk can afford to do precipitately: a couple may marry by special licence and listen to enquiries from their next-of-kin after the fact; they can be precipitate in making children and marry after the event; children will break with their parents and lose themselves in other townships; several parents do not hold coming-out parties to celebrate the last day of a new-born baby's month-long confinement in the house. But death humbles the most unconventional, the hardest rebel. The dead person cannot simply be packed off to the cemetery. You are a person because of other human beings, you are told. The aunt from a distant province will never forgive you if she arrives and finds the deceased buried before she has seen his lifeless face for the last time. Between the death and the funeral, while the body lies in the mortuary (which has to be paid for) there is a wake each night. Day and night relatives and friends and their relatives and their friends come and go, saying words of consolation to the bereaved. And all the time some next-of-kin must act as spokesman to relate the circumstances of death to all who arrive for the first time. Petty intrigues and dramatic scenes among the relatives as they prepare for the funeral are innumerable. Without them, a funeral doesn't look like one.

Talita slept where she sat, on a mattress spread out on the floor in a corner, thinking and saying little, and then only when asked questions like: 'What will you eat now?' or 'Has your headache stopped today?' or 'Are your bowels moving properly?' or 'The burial society wants your marriage certificate, where do you keep it?' Apart from this, she sat or lay down and thought.

Her man was tall, not very handsome, but lovable; an insurance agent who moved about in a car. Most others in the business walked from house to house and used buses and electric trains between townships. But her man's firm was prosperous and after his fifteen years' good service it put a new car at his disposal. Merman had soft gentle eyes and was not at all as vivacious as she. Talita often teased him about his shyness and what she called the weariness in his tongue because he spoke little. But she always prattled on and on, hardly ever short of topics to talk about.

'Ah, you met your match last night, mother-of-Luka,' her man would say, teasingly.

'My what — who?'

'The woman we met at the dance and talked as if you were not there.'

'How was she my match?'

'Don't pretend to be foolish — *hau*, here's a woman! She talked you to a standstill and left you almost wide-mouthed when I rescued you. Anyone who can do that takes the flag.'

'Ach, get away! And anyhow if I don't talk enough my tongue will rot and grow mouldy.'

They had lived through nineteen years of married life that yielded three children and countless bright and cloudy days. It was blissful generally, in spite of the physical and mental violence around them; the privation; police raids; political strikes and attendant clashes between the police and boycotters; death; ten years of low wages during which she experienced a long spell of ill health. But like everybody else Talita and her man stuck it through. They were in an urban township and like everybody else they made their home there. In the midst of all these living conditions, at once in spite and because of them, the people of Corner B alternately clung together desperately and fell away from the centre; like birds that scatter when the tree on which they have gathered is shaken. And yet for each individual life, a new day dawned and set, and each acted out his own drama which the others might never know of or might only get a glimpse of or guess at.

For Talita, there was that little drama which almost blackened things for herself and her man and children. But because they loved each other so intensely, the ugliest bend was well negotiated, and the cloud passed on, the sun shone again. This was when a love letter fell into her hands owing to one of those clumsy things that often happen when lovers become stupid enough to write to each other. Talita wondered about something, as she sat huddled in the corner of her dining-sitting room and looked at the flame of a candle nearby, now quivering, now swaying this way and that and now coming into an erect position as if it lived a separate life from the stick of wax. She wondered how or why it happened that a mistress should entrust a confidential letter to a stupid messenger who in turn sends someone else without telling him to return the letter if the man should be out; why the second messenger should give the letter to her youngest child who then opens it and calls his mother from the bedroom to read it. Accident? Just downright brazen cheek on the part of the mistress . . . !

A hymn was struck and the wake began in earnest. There was singing, praying, singing, preaching in which the deceased was mentioned several times, often in vehement praise of him and his kindness. The room filled rapidly, until the air was one thick choking lump of grief. Once during the evening someone fainted. 'An aunt of the deceased, the one

who loved him most,' a whisper escaped from someone who seemed to know and it was relayed from
mouth to mouth right out into the yard where some
people stood or sat. 'Shame! Shame!' one could hear
the comment from active sympathizers. More than
once during the evening a woman screamed at high
pitch. 'The sister of the deceased,' a whisper escaped,
and it was relayed. 'Shame! Shame!' was the
murmured comment. *'Ao,* God's people!' an old man
exclaimed. During the prayers inside the people outside continued to speak in low tones.

'Have the police caught the boys?'

'No — what, when has a black corpse been
important?'

'But they have been asking questions in Corner B
today.'

'Hm.'

'When's a black corpse been important?'

'Das' right, just ask him.'

'It is Saturday today and if it was a white man
lying there in the mortuary the newspapers would be
screaming about a manhunt morning and evening
since Thursday, the city would be upside down,
God's truth.'

'No look here you men, these boys don't mean to
kill nobody. Their empty stomachs and no work to
do turns their heads on evil things.'

'Ach, you and your politics. Let one of them break
into your house or ra — .'

The speaker broke off short and wiped his mouth
with his hands as if to remove pieces of a foul word
hanging carelessly from his lip.

'Das not the point,' squeaked someone else.

Just then the notes of a moving hymn rolled out of
the room and the men left the subject hanging and

joined enthusiastically in the singing, taking different parts.

Some women were serving tea and sandwiches. A middle-aged man was sitting at a table in a corner of the room. He had an exercise book in front of him, in which he entered the names of those who donated money and the amounts they gave. Such collections were meant to help meet funeral expenses. In fact they went into buying tea, coffee, bread and even groceries for meals served to guests who came from far.

'Who put him there?' asked an uncle of the deceased in an anxious tone, pointing at the money collector.

'Do I know?' an aunt said.

The question was relayed in whispers in different forms. Every one of the next-of-kin denied responsibility. It was soon discovered that the collector had mounted the stool on his own initiative.

'But don't you know that he has long fingers?' the same uncle flung the question in a general direction, just as if it were a loud thought.

'I'm going to tell him to stop taking money. *Hei*, cousin Stoffel, take that exercise book at once, otherwise we shall never know what has happened to the money.' Cousin Stoffel was not fast, but he had a reputation for honesty.

It was generally known that the deposed young man appeared at every death house where he could easily be suspected to be related to the deceased, and invariably used his initiative to take collections and dispose of some of the revenue. But of course several of the folk who came to console Talita could be seen at other vigils and funerals by those who themselves were regular customers. The communal spirit?

Largely. But also they were known to like their drinks very much. So a small fund was usually raised from the collections to buy liquor from a shebeen nearby and bring it to the wake.

Bang in the middle of a hymn a man came into the room and hissed while he made a beckoning sign to someone. Another hiss, yet another. An interested person who was meanly being left out immediately sensed conspiracy and followed those who answered the call. As they went out, they seemed to peel off a layer of the hymn and carry it out with them as they sang while moving out. In some corner of the yard or in the bedroom, a group of men, and sometimes a woman or two, conducted a familiar ritual.

'God's people,' an uncle said solemnly, screwing up his face in an attempt to identify those who had been called. If he saw a stray one or two, he merely frowned but could do nothing about it on such a solemn occasion. The gate-crashers just stood, half-shy and half-sure of themselves, now rubbing a nose, now changing postures.

'God's people, as I was about to say, here is an ox for slaughter.' At this point he introduced a bottle of brandy. One did not simply plant a whole number of bottles on the floor: that was imprudent. 'Cousin Felang came driving it to this house of sorrow. I have been given the honour of slaughtering it, as the uncle of this clan.' With this he uncorked the bottle and served the brandy, taking care to measure with his fingers.

'This will kill the heart for a time so that it does not break from grief. Do not the English say *drown de sorry?*' He belched from deep down his stomach.

And then tongues began to wag. Anecdotes flew as freely as the drinks. And when they could not contain their mirth they laughed. 'Yes, God's people,' one observed, 'the great death is often funny.'

They did not continually take from the collections. If they felt they were still thirsty, someone went round among those he suspected felt the thirst too, and collected money from them to buy more drinks for another bout.

At midnight the people dispersed. The next-of-kin and close friends would alternate in sleeping in Talita's house. They simply huddled against the wall in the same room and covered themselves with blankets.

Talita sat and waited at her corner like a fixture in the house. The children were staying with a relative and would come back on Sunday to see their father for the last time in his coffin. The corpse would be brought home on Saturday afternoon.

Thoughts continued to mill round in Talita's mind. A line of thought continued from where it had been cut off. One might imagine disjointed lines running around in circles. But always she wanted to keep the image of her man in front of her. Just as though it were an insult to the memory of him when the image escaped her even once.

Her man had confessed without making any scene at all. Perhaps it was due to the soft and timid manner in which Talita had asked him about the letter. She said she was sorry she had taken the letter from the child and, even when she had seen that instead of beginning 'Dear Talita' it was 'My everything', she had yielded to the temptation to read it. She was very sorry, she said, and added something to the effect that if she hadn't known, and he continued to carry on with the mistress, it wouldn't have been so bad. But the knowing it . . . Her man had promised

not to see his mistress again. Not that his affair had
detracted in any way from the relationship between
man and wife, or made the man neglect the welfare of
his family. Talita remembered how loyal he had been.
The matter was regarded as closed and life had
proceeded unhaltingly.

A few months later, however, she had noticed
things, almost imperceptible; had heard stray words
outside the house, almost inaudible or insignificant,
which showed that her man was seeing his mistress.
Talita had gone out of her way to track 'the other
woman' down. No one was going to share her man
with her, fullstop, she said to herself.

She had found her: Marta, also a married woman.
One evening Talita, when she was sure she could not
be wrong in her suspicions, had followed Marta from
the railway station to the latter's house in another
part of Corner B. She entered shortly after the un-
suspecting hostess. Marta's husband was in. Talita
greeted both and sat down.

'I am glad you are in, *Morena* — sir. I have just
come to ask you to chain your bitch. That is my man
and mine alone.' She stood up to leave.

'Wait, my sister,' Marta's husband said. 'Marta!' he
called to his wife who had walked off saying,
laughingly and defiantly, 'Aha, ooh,' perhaps to
suppress any feeling of embarrassment, as Talita
thought. She wouldn't come out.

'You know, my sister,' the man said with
disturbing calm, 'you know a bitch often answers to
the sniffing of a male. And I think we both have to
do some fastening.' He gave Talita a piercing look
which made her drop her eyes. She left the house. So
he knows too, she thought. That look he gave her
told her they shared the same apprehensions. Her

man had never talked about the incident, although she was sure that Marta must have told him of it. Or would she have the courage to?

Often there were moments of deep silence as Talita and her man sat together or lay side by side. But he seldom stiffened up. He would take her into his arms and love her furiously and she would respond generously and tenderly, because she loved him and the pathos in his eyes.

'You know, my man,' she ventured to say one evening in bed, 'if there is anything I can help you with, if there is anything you would like to tell me, you mustn't be afraid to tell me. There may be certain things a woman can do for her man which he never suspected she could do.'

'Oh don't worry about me. There is nothing you need do for me.' And, like someone who had at last found a refuge after a rough and dangerous journey, her man would fold her in his arms and love her.

Was this it, she wondered? But how? Did it begin during her long period of ill health — this Marta-thing? Or did it begin with a school episode? How could she tell? Her man never talked about his former boy-girl attachments, except in an oblique or vague way which yielded not a clue. Marta was pretty, no doubt. She was robust, had a firm waist and seemed to possess in physical appearance all that could attract a man. But if she, Talita, failed to give her man something Marta had to offer, she could not trace it. How could she? Her man was not the complaining type, and she often found out things that displeased him herself and set out to put them out of his way if she could. In the morning, while he was asleep, she would stare into his broad face, into his tender eyes, to see if she could read something.

But all she saw was the face she loved. Funny that you saw your man's face every day almost and yet you couldn't look at it while he slept without the sensation of some guilt or something timid or tense or something held in suspension; so that if the man stirred, your heart gave a leap as you turned your face away. One thing she was sure of amidst all the wild and agonizing speculation: her man loved her and their children . . .

'They're always doing this to me I do not matter I cannot allow plans to be made over the body of my cousin without my being told about it and why do they talk behind my back I don't stand for dusty nonsense me. And someone's daughter has the cheek to say I am nobody in the family of my cousin's and says me, I am always going ahead of others yes I am always running ahead of the others because I think other people are fools what right has she to talk behind my back why does she not tell me face to face what she thinks of me she is afraid I can make her see her mother if once I . . . '

'Sh!' The senior uncle of the dead man cut in to try to keep the peace. And he was firm. 'What do you want to turn this house into? There is a widow in there in grief and here you are you haven't got what the English call respection. Do you want all the people around to laugh at us, think little of us? All of us bury our quarrels when we come together to weep over a dear one who has left; what *nawsons* is this?'

The cousin who felt outraged stood against the wall with her hands hidden behind her apron like a child caught in an act of mischief. She had not been addressing herself to anyone in particular and hoped someone would pick up the challenge. And although she felt rebuked, she said, 'But uncle-of-the-clan, these people are always whispering dirty things behind my back what should I say? And then they go and order three buses instead of four these God's people have collected money for us to hire enough buses for them I shall not be surprised if someone helped himself to some of the money — '

'Sh!' the senior uncle interrupted. 'We do not throw urine out of the chamber for everybody to see.'

Someone whispered, *Mapodisa!* Police! With two boys! Everyone in the yard stood still, as if to some command. An African constable came in, preceded by two dirty-looking youngsters in handcuffs.

'Stop,' he barked when they neared the door.

'Where is the widow?' the constable asked, addressing no one in particular.

Silence.

'Hela! Are these people dumb?' Silence. One of the boys blew his nose on to the ground with his free hand and wiped off the stuff from his upper lip and ran the hand down the flank of his trousers.

The constable went into the room with a firm stride, almost lifting the boys clear off the ground in the process. Inside, he came face to face with Talita, who was sitting in her usual corner. She seemed to look through him, and this unsettled him slightly. He braced himself up visibly.

'Face the mother there you fakabond!' he barked at the boys.

'I say look at the mother there, you dirty tsotsi.' He angrily lifted the drooping head of one of them.

'You know this mother?' The boys shook their heads and mumbled.

'Mother, look at these tsotsis. Have you ever seen

them before? Look at them carefully, take your time.'

Talita looked at them wearily. She shook her head.

'Sure-sure?' Again she shook her head.

'I know what you do at night you fakabond.' The whole house was now full of him, the rustle of his khaki uniform and his voice and his official importance. 'You kill, you steal, you rape and give other people no peace. Fakabond! You saw boys attack a man the other night, did you? Dung, let me tell you! You talk dung. Pure dung! You took out your knives for the man, fakabond! You see that bucket in front of your cells? You will fill it in quick time tonight when the baas is finished with you. This big white sergeant doesn't play around with black boys like you as I do. Dung! You didn't mean to kill him, you say, just wanted to beat him up and he fought back. Dung!'

The constable had hardly said the last word when an elderly woman came out of another room, holding a stick for support.

'What is all this?' she asked. 'First you come and shake this poor child out of her peace when she has lost her man and then you use foul words at a time like this. Cannot this business wait until after the burial? Tell me who are you? Who is your father? Where were you born?'

He mumbled a few words, but the woman cut him short.

'Is this how you would like your mother or your wife to be treated, I mean your own own mother?'

'I am doing the government's work.'

'Go and tell that government of yours that he is full of dung to send you to do such things. *Sies! Kgoboromente kgoboromente!* You and him can go to hell where you belong. Get out!'

She took a lunge and landed her stick on him. Once, then twice, and the third time she missed because the constable dashed noisily out of the house, hauling the boys by the handcuffs. The woman pursued him with a limp, right up to the car in which was a white man in plain clothes — directly in front of the gate. The white man was obviously at pains to suppress a laugh. The constable entered with the boys in a most disorderly, undignified manner . . . The vehicle started off amidst the clatter of words that continued to come from the woman's mouth.

Talia wondered: Were the boys merely the arms of some monster sitting in the dark somewhere, wreaking vengeance on her man . . . ?

Evening came. One caucus after another was held to make sure all arrangements were intact; for this was Saturday and the corpse had arrived. The double-decker buses from the city transport garages: were they booked? You son of Kobe did you get the death certificate and permit for the cemetery? And the number plate? They want to see the dead man's pass first. Ask for it in the house . . . Pass pass be damned, cannot a man go to his grave in peace without dragging his chains after him . . . ! Is the pastor coming tonight? Those three goats: have they been slaughtered? Right, this is how men work . . . You have worked well. The caucus meetings went on . . .

Word went round that the grandmother of the deceased had come. She loved Talita, so everyone who mattered testified. Heads nodded. Relatives who had not seen one another for a long long time were there and family bonds were in place again. Some who were enemies tolerated each other, shooting side-glances at each other. Those who loved each other tended to exaggerate and exhibit the fact.

The people came in to keep vigil for the last night. The brown coffin — not ostentatious enough to cause a ripple of tell-tale excitement — stood against a wall. A white sheet was thrown across to partition the room so that in the smaller portion the corpse lay on a mattress under a white sheet. Talita sat next to it, leaning against her man's grandmother. The days and nights of waiting had told on her face; the black head-tie that was fastened like a hood cast a shade over it. Her hair had already been reduced to look like a schoolgirl's with a pair of scissors. Singing began. The elderly ladies washed the corpse. The tune sailed out of the room, floated in the air and was caught by those outside.

'Tomorrow after the funeral eh? O.K.?'

'Yes, tomorrow after the funeral. Where?'

'At the party.'

'Oh-ja, I forgot Cy's party. I'll go home first and change, eh? But I'm scared of my Pa.'

'Let the old beard go fly a kite.'

'He's my Pa all the same.' She pushed him slightly as a reproach.

'O.K. He is, so let's not fight 'bout it. Still don't you want me to come to your house?'

'You know he don't like you and he'd kill me if he saw me with you.'

'Because you work and I don't I'm sure. I'm getting a job Monday that'll fix the old beard.'

'No it's not just a job and it's not you Pa hates.'

'That's funny talk. What then?'

'Just because I'm twenty-three and I shouldn't

have a boy yet.'

'Jesus! Where's the old man been living all these years? Jesus!'

'Doesn't matter, Bee. You're my boy.' She giggled.

'What's funny?'

'Just remembered my Pa asked me the other day who's that he saw me with. I say your name — Bee, I say.'

'And then?'

'And then his face becomes sour and he says Who? I say Bee. He says Where have you heard someone called Bee — *Bee* did you say? I say anybody can call his son what he likes. He says you must be mad or a tsotsi without even a decent name.'

A deep sigh and then: 'That's not funny.' He trembled slightly.

'Don't be cross Bee, you know it means nothing to me what you're called.'

'Sh — they're praying now.'

Two mouths and two tongues suck each other as he presses her against the wall of the shed that served as a fowl-run.

'Hm, they're praying,' but her words are lost in the other's mouth. He feels her all over and she wriggles against him. She allows herself to be floored . . .

A hymn strikes again.

Two figures heave themselves up from the ground, panting. It has been a dark, delicious, fugitive time. They go back and join the singers, almost unnoticed.

The hymn continues. A hymn of hope, of release by death, of refuge for the weary and tormented: a surrender to death once it has been let loose among a flock of sheep. Underlying the poetry of this surrender is the one long and huge irony of endurance.

In another corner of the yard an elderly man was uncorking a bottle of whisky and pouring it into glasses. The sound of it, like water flowing down a rock crevice, was pleasing to the ear as the company squatted in front of the 'priest'. Here my children, kill the heart and as the Englishman says, *drown de sorry*. Ah, you see now . . . Someone, for lack of something important or relevant to say, but out of sheer blissful expectation, sighed: *'Ja Madoda* — yes, men, death is a strange thing. If he came to my house he would ask my woman to give him food any time and he could come any time of night and say I've come to see if you're all right and then we would talk and talk and talk. We were so close. And now he's late, just like that.' And he sobbed and sniffled.

'Ja,' the other sighed in chorus.

A woman screamed in the room and broke into sobs. The others carried her out.

'Quiet child,' a middle-aged woman coaxed. 'Quiet quiet, quiet.' Talita held out. When Sunday dawned she said in her heart God let it pass this time. The final act came and passed . . .

They were all walking away from the grave towards the tarmac path leading to the exit. Suddenly a woman, seemingly from nowhere, went and flung herself on the soft, red damp mound of the new grave. It was Marta. She screamed like one calling a person across a river in flood, knowing the futility of it all. 'Why did you leave me alone?' Marta yelled, her arms thrown over her head. Her legs kicked as she cried unashamedly, like a child whose toy has been wrenched out of his hand. Soon there was one long horizontal gasp as whispered words escaped the crowd, underlining the grotesqueness of the scene. Some stood stolidly, others amused, others outraged.

Two men went and dragged Martha away, while she still cried, 'Come back, come back why did you leave me alone?'

Talita stopped short. She wanted badly to leap clear of the hands that supported her, but she was too weak. The urge strained every nerve, every muscle of her body. The women who supported her whispered to her to ignore the female's theatrics. 'Let us go, child,' they said. 'She wants you to talk.' They propelled Talita towards the black 'family car'.

A few days later, a letter arrived, addressed to Talita. She was walking about in the yard, but was not allowed to go to work or anywhere beyond her gate. The letter was in a bad but legible scrawl and read:

> 'Dear Missis Molamo, I am dropping this few lines for to hoping that you are living good now i want to telling you my hart is sore sore. i hold myselfe bad on the day of youre mans funeral my hart was ful of pane too much and i see myselfe already o Missis Molamo alreaddy doing mad doings i think the gods are beatting me now for holding myselfe as wyle animall forgeef forgeef i pray with all my hart child of the people.'

Talita paused. These wild women who can't even write must needs try to do so in English. She felt the tide of anger and hatred mounting up, flushing her whole body, and then she wondered if she should continue to read. She planted her elbow on the table and supported her head with her hand. She felt drawn to the letter, so she obeyed the impulse to continue.

'now i must tel you something you must noe
quik quik thees that i can see that when you
come to my hause and then whenn you see me
kriing neer the grafe i can see you tyink i am
sweet chokolet of your man i can see you think
in your hart my man love that wooman no no i
want to tel you that he neva love me nevaneva
he livd same haus my femily rented in Fitas and
i lovd him mad i tel you i lovd him mad i wanted
him with red eyes he was nise leetl bit nise to me
but i see he sham for me as i have got no big
ejucashin he got too much book i make nise tea
and cake fo him and he like my muther and he is
so nise i want to foss him to love me but he just
nise i am shoor he come to meet me in toun
now we are 2 marryd peeople bicos he
remember me and muther looked aftar him like
bruther for me he was stil nise to me but al
wooman can see whenn there is no loveness in a
man and they can see lovfulness. now he is gonn
i feel i want to rite with my al ten fingas becos i
have too muche to say aboute your sorriness and
my sorriness i will help you to kry you help me
to kry and leev that man in peas with his gods.
so i stop press here my deer i beg to pen off the
gods look after us

> i remain your sinserity
> Missis Marta Shuping.'

When Talita finished reading, a great dawn was
breaking upon her, and she stood up and made tea
for herself. She felt like a foot traveller after a good
refreshing bath.

Mrs Plum

My madam's name was Mrs Plum. She loved dogs and Africans and said that everyone must follow the law even if it hurt. These were three big things in Madam's life.

I came to work for Mrs Plum in Greenside, not very far from the centre of Johannesburg, after leaving two white families. The first white people I worked for as a cook and laundry woman were a man and his wife in Parktown North. They drank too much and always forgot to pay me. After five months I said to myself, No. I am going to leave these drunks. So that was it. That day I was as angry as a red-hot iron when it meets water. The second house I cooked and washed for had five children who were badly brought up. This was in Belgravia. Many times they called me You Black Girl and I kept quiet. Because their mother heard them and said nothing. Also I was only new from Phokeng my home, very far away near Rustenburg. I wanted to learn and know the white people before I knew how far to go with the others I would work for afterwards. The thing that drove me

mad and made me pack and go was a man who came
to visit them often. They said he was a cousin or
something like that. He came to the kitchen many
times and tried to make me laugh. He patted me on
the buttocks. I told the master. The man did it again
and I asked the madam that very day to give me my
money and let me go.

These were the first nine months after I had left
Phokeng to work in Johannesburg. There were many
of us girls and young women from Phokeng, from
Zeerust, from Shuping, from Kosten, and many other
places who came to work in the cities. So the suburbs
were full of blackness. Most of us had already passed
Standard Six and so we learned more English where
we worked. None of us likes to work for white
farmers, because we know too much about them on
the farms near our homes. They do not pay well and
they are cruel people.

At Easter time so many of us went home for a long
weekend to see our people and to eat chicken and
sour milk and *morogo* — wild spinach. We also took
home sugar and condensed milk and tea and coffee
and sweets and custard powder and tinned foods.

It was a home-girl of mine, Chimane, who called
me to take a job in Mrs Plum's house, just next door
to where she worked. This is the third year now. I
have been quite happy with Mrs Plum and her
daughter Kate. By this I mean that my place as a
servant in Greenside is not as bad as that of many
others. Chimane too does not complain much. We are
paid six pounds a month with free food and free
servant's room. No one can ever say that they are well
paid, so we go on complaining somehow. Whenever
we meet on Thursday afternoons, which is time-off
for all of us black women in the suburbs, we talk and

talk and talk: about our people at home and their
letters; about their illnesses; about bad crops; about a
sister who wanted a school uniform and books and
school fees; about some of our madams and masters
who are good, or stingy with money or food, or
stupid or full of nonsense, or who kill themselves and
each other, or who are dirty — and so many things I
cannot count them all.

Thursday afternoons we go to town to look at the
shops, to attend a women's club, to see our boy
friends, to go to bioscope some of us. We turn up
smart, to show others the clothes we bought from the
black men who sell soft goods to servants in the
suburbs. We take a number of things and they come
round every month for a bit of money until we finish
paying. Then we dress the way of many white
madams and girls. I think we look really smart.
Sometimes we catch the eyes of a white woman
looking at us and we laugh and laugh and laugh until
we nearly drop onto the ground because we feel good
inside ourselves.

What did the girl next door call you, Mrs Plum asked
me the first day I came to her. Jane, I replied. Was
there not an African name? I said yes, Karabo. All
right, Madam said. We'll call you Karabo, she said.
She spoke as if she knew a name is a big thing. I
knew so many whites who did not care what they
called black people as long as it was all right for their
tongue. This pleased me, I mean Mrs Plum's use of
Karabo; because the only time I heard the name was
when I was at home or when my friends spoke to me.
Then she showed me what to do: meals, meal times,
washing, and where all the things were that I was
going to use.

My daughter will be here in the evening, Madam
said. She is at school. When the daughter came, she
added, she would tell me some of the things she
wanted me to do for her every day.

Chimane, my friend next door, had told me about
the daughter Kate, how wild she seemed to be, and
about Mr Plum who had killed himself with a gun in a
house down the street. They had left the house and
come to this one.

Madam is a tall woman. Not slender, not fat. She
moves slowly, and speaks slowly. Her face looks very
wise, her forehead seems to tell me she has a strong
liver: she is not afraid of anything. Her eyes are
always swollen at the lower eyelids like a white
person who has not slept for many many nights or
like a large frog. Perhaps it is because she smokes too
much, like wet wood that will not know whether to
go up in flames or stop burning. She looks me straight
in the eyes when she talks to me, and I know she does
this with other people too. At first this made me fear
her, now I am used to her. She is not a lazy woman,
and she does many things outside, in the city and in
the suburbs.

This was the first thing her daughter Kate told me
when she came and we met. Don't mind mother, Kate
told me. She said, She is sometimes mad with people
for very small things. She will soon be all right and
speak nicely to you again.

Kate, I like her very much, and she likes me too.
She tells me many things a white woman does not tell
a black servant. I mean things about what she likes
and does not like, what her mother does or does not
do, all these. At first I was unhappy and wanted to
stop her, but now I do not mind.

Kate looks very much like her mother in the face. I

think her shoulders will be just as round and strong-looking. She moves faster than Madam. I asked her why she was still at school when she was so big. She laughed. Then she tried to tell me that the school where she was was for big people, who had finished with lower school. She was learning big things about cooking and food. She can explain better, me I cannot. She came home on weekends.

Since I came to work for Mrs Plum Kate has been teaching me plenty of cooking. I first learned from her and Madam the word *recipes.* When Kate was at the big school, Madam taught me how to read cookery books. I went on very slowly at first, slower than an ox-wagon. Now I know more. When Kate came home, she found I had read the recipe she left me. So we just cooked straightaway. Kate thinks I am fit to cook in a hotel. Madam thinks so too. Never never, I thought. Cooking in a hotel is like feeding oxen. No one can say thank you to you. After a few months I could cook the Sunday lunch and later I could cook specials for Madam's or Kate's guests.

Madam did not only teach me cooking. She taught me how to look after guests. She praised me when I did very very well, not like the white people I had worked for before. I do not know what runs crooked in the heads of other people. Madam also had classes in the evenings for servants to teach them how to read and write. She and two other women in Greenside taught in a church hall.

As I say, Kate tells me plenty of things about Madam. She says to me she says, My mother goes to meetings many times. I ask her I say, What for? She says to me she says, For your people. I ask her I say, My people are in Phokeng far away. They have got mouths, I say. Why does she want to say something

for them? Does she know what my mother and what
my father want to say? They can speak when they
want to. Kate raises her shoulders and drops them
and says, How can I tell you Karabo? I don't say your
people — your family only. I mean all the black
people in this country. I say Oh! What do the black
people want to say? Again she raises her shoulders
and drops them, taking a deep breath.

I ask her I say, With whom is she in the meeting?

She says, With other people who think like her.

I ask her I say, Do you say there are people in the
world who think the same things?

She nods her head.

I ask, What things?

So that a few of your people should one day be
among those who rule this country, get more money
for what they do for the white man and — what did
Kate say again? Yes, that Madam and those who
think like her also wanted my people who have been
to school to choose those who must speak for them
in the — I think she said it looks like a *Kgotla* at
home who rule the villages.

I say to Kate I say, Oh I see now. I say, Tell me
Kate why is madam always writing on the machine,
all the time everyday nearly?

She replies she says, Oh my mother is writing
books.

I ask, You mean a book like those? — pointing at
the books on the shelves.

Yes, Kate says.

And she told me how Madam wrote books and
other things for newspapers and she wrote for the
newspapers and magazines to say things for the black
people who should be treated well, be paid more
money, for the black people who can read and write

many things to choose those who want to speak for them.

Kate also told me she said, My mother and other women who think like her put on black belts over their shoulders when they are sad and they want to show the white government they do not like the things being done by whites to blacks. My mother and the others go and stand where the people in government are going to enter or go out of a building.

I ask her I say, Does the government and the white people listen and stop their sins? She says No. But my mother is in another group of white people.

I ask, Do the people of the government give the women tea and cakes? Kate says, Karabo, how stupid! oh!

I say to her I say, Among my people if someone comes and stands in front of my house I tell him to come in and I give him food. You white people are wonderful. But they keep standing there and the government people do not give them anything.

She replies, You mean strange. How many times have I taught you not to say *wonderful* when you mean *strange!* Well, Kate says with a short heart and looking cross and she shouts, Well they do not stand there the whole day to ask for tea and cakes stupid. Oh dear!

Always when Madam finished to read her newspapers she gave them to me to read to help me speak and write better English. When I had read she asked me to tell her some of the things in it. In this way, I did better and better and my mind was opening and opening and I was learning and learning many things about the black people inside and outside the towns which I did not know in the least. When I found words that were too difficult or I did not understand some of the things I asked Madam. She always told me You see this, you see that, eh? with a heart that can carry on a long way. Yes, Madam writes many letters to the papers. She is always sore about the way the white police beat up black people; about the way black people who work for whites are made to sit at the Zoo Lake with their hearts hanging, because the white people say our people are making noise on Sunday afternoon when they want to rest in their houses and gardens; about many ugly things that happen when some white people meet black man on the pavement or street. So madam writes to the papers to let others know, to ask the government to be kind to us.

In the first year Mrs Plum wanted me to eat at table with her. It was very hard, one because I was not used to eating at table with a fork and knife, two because I heard of no other kitchen worker who was handled like this. I was afraid. Afraid of everybody, of Madam's guests if they found me doing this. Madam said I must not be silly. I must show that African servants can also eat at table. Number three, I could not eat some of the things I loved very much: mealie-meal porridge with sour milk or *morogo*, stamped mealies mixed with butter beans, sour porridge for breakfast and other things. Also, except for morning porridge, our food is nice when you eat with the hand. So nice that it does not stop in the mouth or the throat to greet anyone before it passes smoothly down.

We often had lunch together with Chimane next-door and our garden boy — Ha! I must remember never to say *boy* again when I talk about a man. This makes me think of a day during the first few weeks in Mrs Plum's house. I was talking about Dick her garden man and I said 'garden boy'. And she says to me she says Stop talking about a 'boy', Karabo. Now listen here, she says, you Africans must learn to speak properly about each other. And she says White people won't talk kindly about you if you look down upon each other.

I say to her I say Madam, I learned the word from the white people I worked for, and all the kitchen maids say 'boy'.

She replies she says to me, Those are white people who know nothing, just low-class whites. I say to her I say I thought white people know everything.

She said, You'll learn my girl and you must start in this house, hear? She left me there thinking, my mind mixed up.

I learned. I grew up.

If any woman or girl does not know the Black Crow Club in Bree Street, she does not know anything. I think nearly everything takes place inside and outside that house. It is just where the dirty part of the City begins, with factories and the market. After the market is the place where Indians and 'coloured' people live. It is also at the Black Crow that the buses turn round and go back to the black townships. Noise, noise, noise all the time. There are women who sell hot sweet potatoes and fruit and monkey nuts and boiled eggs in the winter, boiled mealies and the other things in the summer, all these on the pavements. The streets are always full of potato and fruit skins and monkey nut shells. There is always a strong smell of roast pork. I think it is because of Piel's cold storage down Bree Street.

Madam said she knew the black people who work in the Black Crow. She was happy that I was spending my afternoon on Thursdays in such a club. You will learn sewing, knitting, she said, and other things that you like. Do you like to dance? I told her I said, Yes, I want to learn. She paid the two shillings fee for me each month.

We waited on the first floor, we were the ones who were learning sewing; waiting for the teacher. We talked and laughed about madams and masters, and their children and their dogs and birds and whispered about our boy friends.

Sies! My Madam you do not know — *mojuta oa'nete* — a real miser . . .

Jo — jo — jo! you should see our new dog. A big thing like this. People! Big in a foolish way . . .

What! Me, I take a master's bitch by the leg, me, and throw it away so that it keeps howling, *tjwe — tjwe! ngo — wu ngo — wy!* I don't play about with them, me . . .

Shame, poor thing! God sees you, true . . . !

They wanted me to take their dog out for a walk every afternoon and I told them I said It is not my work in other houses the garden man does it. I just said to myself I said they can go to the chickens. Let them bite their elbow before I take out a dog, I am not so mad yet . . .

Hei! It is not like the child of my white people who keeps a big white rat and you know what? He puts it on his bed when he goes to school. And let the blankets just begin to smell of urine and all the nonsense and they tell me to wash them. *Hei,* people!

Did you hear about Rebone, people? Her Madam put her out, because her master was always tapping her buttocks with his fingers. And yesterday the madam saw the master press Rebone against himself . . .

Jo — jo — jo! people . . . !
Dirty white man!
No, not dirty. The madam smells too old for him.
Hei! Go and wash your mouth with soap, this girl's
mouth is dirty . . .
Jo, Rebone, daughter of the people! We must help
her to find a job before she thinks of going back
home.

The teacher came. A woman with strong legs, a
strong face, and kind eyes. She had short hair and
dressed in a simple but lovely floral frock. She stood
well on her legs and hips. She had a black mark
between the two top front teeth. She smiled as if we
were her children. Our group began with games, and
then Lilian Ngoyi took us for sewing. After this she
gave a brief talk to all of us from the different classes.

I can never forget the things this woman said and
how she put them to us. She told us that the time had
passed for black girls and women in the suburbs to be
satisfied with working, sending money to our people
and going to see them once a year. We were to learn,
she said, that the world would never be safe for black
people until they were in the government with the
power to make laws. The power should be given by
the Africans who were more than whites.

We asked her questions and she answered them
with wisdom. I shall put some of them down in my
own words as I remember them.

Shall we take the place of the white people in the
government?

Some yes. But we shall be more than they as we
are more in the country. But also the people of all
colours will come together and there are good white
men we can choose and there are Africans some white
people will choose to be in the government.

There are good madams and masters and bad ones. Should we take the good ones for friends?

A master and a servant can never be friends. Never, so put that out of your head, will you! You are not even sure if the ones you say are good are not like that because they cannot breathe or live without the work of your hands. As long as you need their money, face them with respect. But you must know that many sad things are happening in our country and you, all of you, must always be learning, adding what you already know, and obey us when we ask you to help us.

At other times Lilian Ngoyi told us she said, Remember your poor people at home and the way in which the whites are moving them from place to place like sheep and cattle. And at other times again she told us she said, Remember that a hand cannot wash itself, it needs another to do it.

I always thought of Madam when Lilian Ngoyi spoke. I asked myself, What would she say if she knew that I was listening to such words. Words like: A white man is looked after by his black nanny and his mother when he is a baby. When he grows up the white government looks after him, sends him to school, makes it impossible for him to suffer from the great hunger, keeps job ready and open for him as soon as he wants to leave school. Now Lilian Ngoyi asked she said, How many white people can be born in a white hospital, grow up in white streets be clothed in lovely cotton, lie on white cushions; how many whites can live all their lives in a fenced place away from people of other colours and then, as men and women learn quickly the correct ways of thinking, learn quickly to ask questions in their minds, big questions that will throw over all the nice things of a white man's life? How many? Very very few! For those who have begun and are joining us with both feet in our house, we can only say Welcome!

I was learning. I was growing up. Every time I thought of Madam, she became more and more like a dark forest which one fears to enter, and which one will never know. But there were several times when I thought, This woman is easy to understand, she is like all the other white women.

What else are they teaching you at the Black Crow, Karabo?

I tell her I say, nothing, Madam. I ask her I say Why does Madam ask?

You are changing.

What does Madam mean?

Well, you are changing.

But we are always changing Madam.

And she left me standing in the kitchen. This was a few days after I had told her that I did not want to read more than one white paper a day. The only magazines I wanted to read, I said to her, were those from overseas, if she had them. I told her that white papers had pictures of white people most of the time. They talked mostly about white people and their gardens, dogs, weddings and parties. I asked her if she could buy me a Sunday paper that spoke about my people. Madam bought it for me. I did not think that she would do it.

There were mornings when, after hanging the white people's washing on the line Chimane and I stole a little time to stand at the fence and talk. We always stood where we could be hidden by our rooms.

Hei, Karabo, you know what? That was Chimane.

No — what? Before you start, tell me, has Timi

come back to you?

Ach, I do not care. He is still angry. But boys are fools they always come back dragging themselves on their empty bellies. *Hei* you know what?

Yes?

The Thursday past I saw Moruti K.K. I laughed until I dropped on the ground. He is standing in front of the Black Crow. I believe his big stomach was crying from hunger. Now he has a small dog in his armpit, and is standing before a woman selling boiled eggs and — *hei* home-girl! — tripe and intestines are boiling in a pot — oh, — the smell, you could fill a hungry belly with it, the way it was good. I think Moruti K.K. is waiting for the woman to buy a boiled egg. I do not know what the woman was still doing. I am standing nearby. The dog keeps wriggling and pushing out its nose, looking at the boiling tripe. Moruti keeps patting it with his free hand, not so? Again the dog wants to spill out of Moruti's hand and it gives a few sounds through the nose. *Hei* man, home-girl! One two three the dog spills out to catch some of the good meat! It misses falling into the hot gravy in which the tripe is swimming I do not know how. Moruti K.K. tries to chase it. It has tumbled on to the women's eggs and potatoes and all are in the dust. She stands up and goes after K.K. She is shouting to him to pay, not so? Where am I at that time? I am nearly dead with laughter the tears are coming down so far.

I was myself holding tight on the fence so as not to fall through laughing. I held my stomach to keep back a pain in the side.

I ask her I say, Did Moruti K.K. come back to pay for the wasted food?

Yes, he paid.

The dog?

He caught it. That is a good African dog. A dog must look for its own food when it is not time for meals. Not these stupid spoiled angels the whites keep giving tea and biscuits.

Hmm.

Dick our garden man joined us, as he often did. When the story was repeated to him the man nearly rolled on the ground laughing.

He asks who is Reverend K.K.?

I say he is the owner of the Black Crow.

Oh!

We reminded each other, Chimane and I, of the round minister. He would come into the club, look at us with a smooth smile on his smooth round face. He would look at each one of us, with that smile on all the time, as if he had forgotten that it was there. Perhaps he had, because as he looked at us, almost stripping us naked with his watery shining eyes — funny — he could have been a farmer looking at his ripe corn, thinking many things.

K.K. often spoke without shame about what he called ripe girls — *matjitjana* — with good firm breasts. He said such girls were pure without any nonsense in their heads and bodies. Everybody talked a great deal about him and what they thought he must be doing in his office whenever he called in so-and-so.

The Reverend K.K. did not belong to any church. He baptised, married, and buried people for a fee, who had no church to do such things for them. They said he had been driven out of the Presbyterian Church. He had formed his own, but it did not go far. Later he came and opened the Black Crow. He knew just how far to go with Lilian Ngoyi. She said

although she used his club to teach us things that
would help us in life, she could not go on if he was
doing any wicked things with the girls in his office.
Moruti K.K. feared her, and kept his place.

When I began to tell my story I thought I was going
to tell you mostly about Mrs Plum's two dogs. But I
have been talking about people. I think Dick is right
when he says What is a dog! And there are so many
dogs cats and parrots in Greenside and other places
that Mrs Plum's dogs do not look special. But there
was something special in the dog business in Madam's
house. The way in which she loved them, maybe.

Monty is a tiny animal with long hair and small
black eyes and a face nearly like that of an old
woman. The other, Malan, is a bit bigger, with brown
and white colours. It has small hair and looks naked
by the side of his friend. They sleep in two separate
baskets which stay in Madam's bedroom. They are to
be washed often and brushed and sprayed and they
sleep on pink linen. Monty has a pink ribbon which
stays on his neck most of the time. They both carry a
cover on their backs. They make me fed up when I
see them in their baskets, looking fat, and as if they
knew all that was going on everywhere.

It was Dick's work to look after Monty and Malan,
to feed them, and to do everything for them. He did
this together with garden work and cleaning of the
house. He came at the beginning of this year. He just
came, as if from nowhere, and Madam gave him the
job as she had chased away two before him, she told
me. In both those cases, she said that they could not
look after Monty and Malan.

Dick had a long heart, even although he told me
and Chimane that European dogs were stupid,

spoiled. He said, one day those white people will put
ear rings and toe rings and bangles on their dogs. That
would be the day he would leave Mrs Plum. For, he
said, he was sure that she would want him to polish
the rings and bangles with Brasso.

Although he had a long heart, Madam was still not
sure of him. She often went to the dogs after a meal
or after a cleaning and said to them Did Dick give you
food sweethearts? Or, Did Dick wash you sweethearts? Let me see. And I could see that Dick was
blowing up like a balloon with anger. These things
called white people! he said to me. Talking to dogs!

I say to him I say, People talk to oxen at home do
I not say so?

Yes, he says, but at home do you not know that a
man speaks to an ox because he wants to make it pull
the plough or the wagon or to stop or to stand still
for a person to inspan it. No one simply goes to an ox
looking at him with eyes far apart and speaks to it.
Let me ask you, do you ever see a person where we
come from take a cow and press it to his stomach or
his cheek? Tell me!

And I say to Dick I say, We were talking about an
ox, not a cow.

He laughed with his broad mouth until tears came
out of his eyes. At a certain point I laughed aloud
too.

One day when you have time, Dick says to me, he
says, you should look into Madam's bedroom when
she has put a notice outside her door.

Dick, what are you saying, I ask.

I do not talk, me. I know deep inside me.

Dick was about our age, I and Chimane. So we
always said *moshiman'o* when we spoke about his
tricks. Because he was not too big to be a boy to us.

He also said to us *Hei, lona banyana kelona* — Hey
you girls, you! His large mouth always seemed to be
making ready to laugh. I think Madam did not like
this. Many times she would say What is there to make
you laugh here? Or in the garden she would say This
is a flower and when it wants water that is not funny!
Or again, If you did more work and stopped trying
to water my plants with your smile you would be
more useful. Even when Dick did not mean to smile.
What Madam did not get tired of saying was, If I left
you to look after my dogs without anyone to look
after you at the same time you would drown the poor
things.

   Dick smiled at Mrs Plum. Dick hurt Mrs Plum's
dogs? Then cows can fly. He was really — really afraid
of white people, Dick. I think he tried very hard not
to feel afraid. For he was always showing me and
Chimane in private how Mrs Plum walked, and spoke.
He took two bowls and pressed them to his chest,
speaking softly to them as Madam speaks to Monty
and Malan. Or he sat at Madam's table and acted the
way she sits when writing. Now and again he looked
back over his shoulder, pulled his face long like a
horse's making as if he were looking over his glasses
while telling me something to do. Then he would sit
on one of the armchairs, cross his legs and act the
way Madam drank her tea; he held the cup he was
thinking about between his thumb and pointing
finger, only letting their nails meet. And he laughed
after every act. He did these things, of course, when
Madam was not home. And where was I at such
times? Almost flat on my stomach, laughing.

   But oh how Dick trembled when Mrs Plum scolded
him! He did his house-cleaning very well. Whatever
mistake he made, it was mostly with the dogs; their

linen, their food. One white man came into the house
one afternoon to tell Madam that Dick had been very
careless when taking the dogs out for a walk. His own
dog was waiting on Madam's stoep. He repeated that
he had been driving down our street and Dick had let
loose Monty and Malan to cross the street. The white
man made plenty of noise about this and I think
wanted to let Madam know how useful he had been.
He kept on saying Just one inch, *just* one inch. It was
lucky I put on my brakes quick enough . . . But your
boy kept on smiling — Why? Strange. My boy would
only do it twice and only twice and then . . . ! His
pass. The man moved his hand like one writing, to
mean that he would sign his servant's pass for him to
go and never come back. When he left, the white man
said Come on Rusty, the boy is waiting to clean you.
Dogs with names, men without, I thought.

Madam climbed on top of Dick for this, as we say.

Once one of the dogs, I don't know which — Malan
or Monty — took my stocking — brand new, you hear
— and tore it with its teeth and paws. When I told
Madam about it, my anger as high as my throat, she
gave me money to buy another pair. It happened
again. This time she said she was not going to give me
money because I must also keep my stockings where
the two gentlemen would not reach them. Mrs Plum
did not want us ever to say *Voetsek* when we wanted
the dogs to go away. Me I said this when they came
sniffing at my legs or fingers. I hate it.

In my third year in Mrs Plum's house, many things
happened, most of them all bad for her. There was
trouble with Kate; Chimane had big trouble; my heart
was twisted by two loves; and Monty and Malan
became real dogs for a few days.

Madam had a number of suppers and parties. She

invited Africans to some of them. Kate told me the
reasons for some of the parties. Like her mother's
books when finished, a visitor from across the seas
and so on. I did not like the black people who came
here to drink and eat. They spoke such difficult
English like people who were full of all the books in
the world. They looked at me as if I were right down
there whom they thought little of — me a black
person like them.

One day I heard Kate speak to her mother. She
says I don't know why you ask so many Africans to
the house. A few will do at a time. She said something about the government which I could not hear
well. Madam replies she says to her You know some
of them do not meet white people often, so far away
in their dark houses. And she says to Kate that they
do not come because they want her as a friend but
they just want a drink for nothing.

I simply felt that I could not be the servant of
white people and of blacks at the same time. At my
home or in my room I could serve them without a
feeling of shame. And now, if they were only coming
to drink!

But one of the black men and his sister always
came to the kitchen to talk to me. I must have looked
unfriendly the first time, for Kate talked to me about
it afterwards as she was in the kitchen when they
came. I know that at that time I was not easy at all. I
was ashamed and I felt that a white person's house
was not the place for me to look happy in front of
other black people while the white man looked on.

Another time it was easier. The man was alone. I
shall never forget that night, as long as I live. He
spoke kind words and I felt my heart grow big inside
me. It caused me to tremble. There were several other

visits. I knew that I loved him, I could never know
what he really thought of me, I mean as a woman and
he as a man. But I loved him, and I still think of him
with a sore heart. Slowly I came to know the pain of
it. Because he was a doctor and so full of knowledge
and English I could not reach him. So I knew he
could not stoop down to see me as someone who
wanted him to love me.

Kate turned very wild. Mrs Plum was very much
worried. Suddenly it looked as if she were a new
person, with new ways and new everything. I do not
know what was wrong or right. She began to play the
big gramophone aloud, as if the music were for the
whole of Greenside. The music was wild and she
twisted her waist all the time, with her mouth half
open. She did the same things in her room. She left
the big school and every Saturday night now she went
out. When I looked at her face, there was something
deep and wild there on it, and when I thought she
looked young she looked old, and when I thought she
looked old she was young. We were both 22 years of
age. I think that I could se the reason why her mother
was so worried, why she was suffering.

Worse was to come.

They were now openly screaming at each other.
They began in the sitting room and went upstairs
together, speaking fast hot biting words, some of
which I did not grasp. One day Madam comes to me
and says You know Kate loves an African, you know
the doctor who comes to supper here often. She says
he loves her too and they will leave the country and
marry outside. Tell me, Karabo, what do your people
think of this kind of thing between a white woman
and a black man? It *cannot* be right is it?

I reply and I say to her We have never seen it

happen before where I come from.

That's right, Karabo, it is just madness.

Madam left. She looked like a hunted person.

These white women, I say to myself I say these white women, why do not they love their own men and leave us to love ours!

From that minute I knew that I would never want to speak to Kate. She appeared to me as a thief, as a fox that falls upon a flock of sheep at night. I hated her. To make it worse, he would never be allowed to come to the house again.

Whenever she was home there was silence between us. I no longer wanted to know anything about what she was doing, where or how.

I lay awake for hours on my bed. Lying like that, I seemed to feel parts of my body beat and throb inside me, the way I have seen big machines doing, pounding and pounding and pushing and pulling and pouring some water into one hole which came out at another end. I stretched myself so many times so as to feel tired and sleepy.

When I did sleep, my dreams were full of painful things.

One evening I made up my mind, after putting it off many times. I told my boy-friend that I did not want him any longer. He looked hurt, and that hurt me too. He left.

The thought of the African doctor was still with me and it pained me to know that I should never see him again, unless I met him in the street on a Thursday afternoon. But he had a car. Even if I did meet him by luck, how could I make him see that I loved him? Ach, I do not believe he would even stop to think what kind of woman I am. Part of that winter was a time of longing and burning for me. I

say part because there are always things to keep
servants busy whose white people go to the sea for
the winter.

To tell the truth, winter was the time for servants;
not nannies, because they went with their madams so
as to look after the children. Those like me stayed
behind to look after the house and dogs. In winter so
many families went away that the dogs remained the
masters and madams. You could see them walk like
white people in the streets. Silent but with plenty of
power. And when you saw them you knew that they
were full of more nonsense and fancies in the house.

There was so little work to do.

One week word was whispered round that a home-
boy of ours was going to hold a party in his room on
Saturday. I think we all took it for a joke. How could
the man be so bold and stupid? The police were
always driving about at night looking for black
people; and if the whites next door heard the party
noise — *oho!* But still, we were full of joy and wanted
to go. As for Dick, he opened his big mouth and
nearly fainted when he heard of it and that I was
really going.

During the day on the big Saturday Kate came.

She seemed a little less wild. But I was not ready to
talk to her. I was surprised to hear myself answer her
when she said to me Mother says you do not like a
marriage between a white girl and a black man,
Karabo.

Then she was silent.

She says But I want to help him, Karabo.

I ask her I say You want to help him to do what?

To go higher and higher, to the top.

I knew I wanted to say so much that was boiling in
my chest. I could not say it. I thought of Lilian Ngoyi

at the Black Crow, what she said to us. But I was
mixed up in my head and in my blood.

You still agree with my mother?

All I could say was I said to your mother I had
never seen a black man and a white woman marrying,
you hear me? What I think about it is my business.

I remembered that I wanted to iron my party dress
and so I left her. My mind was full of the party again
and I was glad because Kate and the doctor would
not worry my peace that day. And the next day the
sun would shine for all of us, Kate or no Kate,
doctor or no doctor.

The house where our home-boy worked was
hidden from the main road by a number of trees. But
although we asked a number of questions and
counted many fingers of bad luck until we had no
more hands for fingers, we put on our best pay-while-
you-wear dresses and suits and clothes bought from
boys who had stolen them, and went to our home-
boy's party. We whispered all the way while we
climbed up to the house. Someone who knew told us
that the white people next door were away for the
winter. Oh, so that is the thing, we said.

We poured into the garden through the back and
stood in front of his room laughing quietly. He came
from the big house behind us, and were we not struck
dumb when he told us to go into the white people's
house! Was he mad? We walked in with slow footsteps that seemed to be sniffing at the floor, not sure
of anything. Soon we were standing and sitting all
over on the nice warm cushions and the heaters were
on. Our home-boy turned the lights low. I counted
fifteen people inside. We saw how we loved one
another's evening dress. The boys were smart too.

Our home-boy's girl-friend Naomi was busy in the

kitchen preparing food. He took out glasses and cold drinks — fruit juice, tomato juice, ginger beers, and so many other kinds of soft drink. It was just too nice. The tarts, the biscuits, the snacks, the cakes, *woo*, that was a party, I tell you. I think I ate more ginger cake than I had ever done in my life. Naomi had baked some of the things. Our home-boy came to me and said I do not want the police to come here and have reason to arrest us, so I am not serving hot drinks, not even beer. There is no law that we cannot have parties, is there? So we can feel free. Our use of this house is the master's business. If I had asked him he would have thought me mad.

I say to him I say, You have a strong liver to do such a thing.

He laughed.

He played pennywhistle music on gramophone records — Miriam Makeba, Dorothy Masuka and other African singers and players. We danced and the party became more and more noisy and more happy. *Hai*, those girls Miriam and Dorothy, they can sing, I tell you! We ate more and more and told more stories. In the middle of the party, our home-boy called us to listen to what he was going to say. Then he told us how he and a friend of his in Orlando collected money to bet on a horse for the July Handicap in Durban. They did this each year but lost. Now they had won two hundred pounds. We all clapped hands and cheered. Two hundred pounds *woo!*

You should go and sit at home and just eat time, I say to him. He laughs and says You have no understanding not one little bit.

To all of us he says Now my brothers and sisters enjoy yourselves. At home I should slaughter a goat for us to feast and thank our ancestors. But this is town life and we must thank them with tea and cake and all those sweet things. I know some people think I must be so bold that I could be midwife to a lion that is giving birth, but enjoy yourselves and have no fear.

Madam came back looking strong and fresh.

The very week she arrived the police had begun again to search servants' rooms. They were looking for what they called loafers and men without passes who they said were living with friends in the suburbs against the law. Our dog's meat boys became scarce because of the police. A boy who had a girl-friend in the kitchens, as we say, always told his friends that he was coming for dog's meat when he meant he was visiting his girl. This was because we gave our boy-friends part of the meat the white people bought for the dogs and us.

One night a white and a black policeman entered Mrs Plum's yard. They said they had come to search. She says no, they cannot. They say Yes, they must do it. She answers No. They forced their way to the back, to Dick's room and mine. Mrs Plum took the hose that was running in the front garden and quickly went round to the back. I cut across the floor to see what she was going to say to the men. They were talking to Dick, using dirty words. Mrs Plum did not wait, she just pointed the hose at the two policemen. This seemed to surprise them. They turned round and she pointed it into their faces. Without their seeing me I went to the tap at the corner of the house and opened it more. I could see Dick, like me, was trying to keep down his laughter. They shouted and tried to wave the water away, but she kept the hose pointing at them, now moving it up and down. They turned and ran through the back gate, swearing the while.

That fixes them, Mrs Plum said.

The next day the morning paper reported it.

They arrived in the afternoon — the two policemen — with another. They pointed out Mrs Plum and she was led to the police station. They took her away to answer for stopping the police while they were doing their work.

She came back and said she had paid bail.

At the magistrate's court, Madam was told that she had done a bad thing. She would have to pay a fine or else go to prison for fourteen days. She said she would go to jail to show that she felt she was not in the wrong.

Kate came and tried to tell her that she was doing something silly going to jail for a small thing like that. She tells Madam she says This is not even a thing to take to the high court. Pay the money. What is £5?

Madam went to jail.

She looked very sad when she came out. I thought of what Lilian Ngoyi often said to us: You must be ready to go to jail for the things you believe are true and for which you are taken by the police. What did Mrs Plum really believe about me, Chimane, Dick and all the other black people, I asked myself. I did not know. But from all those things she was writing for the papers and all those meetings she was going to where white people talked about black people and the way they are treated by the government, from what those white women with black bands over their shoulders were doing standing where a white government man was going to pass, I said to myself I said This woman, *hai*, I do not know she seems to think very much of us black people. But why was she so sad?

Kate came back home to stay after this. She still
played the big gramophone loud-loud-loud and
twisted her body at her waist until I thought it was
going to break. Then I saw a young white man come
often to see her. I watched them through the opening
near the hinges of the door between the kitchen and
the sitting room where they sat. I saw them kiss each
other for a long long time. I saw him lift up Kate's
dress and her white-white legs begin to tremble, and
— oh I am afraid to say more, my heart was beating
hard. She called him Jim. I thought it was funny
because white people in the shops call black men Jim.

Kate had begun to play with Jim when I met a boy
who loved me and I loved. He was much stronger
than the one I sent away and I loved him more, much
more. The face of the doctor came to my mind often,
but it did not hurt me so any more. I stopped looking
at Kate and her Jim through openings. We spoke to
each other, Kate and I, almost as freely as before but
not quite. She and her mother were friends again.

Hello, Karabo, I heard Chimane call me one
morning as I was starching my apron. I answered. I
went to the line to hang it. I saw she was standing at
the fence, so I knew she had something to tell me. I
went to her.

Hello!

Hello, Chimane!

O kae?

Ke teng. Wena?

At that moment a woman came out through the
back door of the house where Chimane was working.

I have not seen that one before, I say, pointing
with my head.

Chimane looked back. Oh, that one. *Hei*, daughter-
of-the-people, *Hei*, you have not seen miracles. You

know this is Madam's mother-in-law as you see her there. Did I never tell you about her?

White people, nonsense. You know what? That poor woman is here now for two days. She has to cook for herself and I cook for the family.

On the same stove?

Yes, she comes after me when I have finished.

She had her own food to cook?

Yes, Karabo. White people have no heart no sense.

What will eat them up if they share their food?

Ask me, just ask me. God! She clapped her hands to show that only God knew, and it was His business, not ours.

Chimane asks me she says, Have you heard from home?

I tell her I say, Oh daughter-of-the-people, more and more deaths. Something is finishing the people at home. My mother has written. She says they are all right, my father too and my sisters, except for the people who have died. Malebo, the one who lived alone in the house I showed you last year, a white house, he is gone. Then teacher Sedimo. He was very thin and looked sick all the time. He taught my sisters not me. His mother-in-law you remember I told you died last year — *no*, the year before. Mother says also there is a woman she does not think I remember because I last saw her when I was a small girl she passed away in Zeerust she was my mother's greatest friend when they were girls. She would have gone to her burial if it was not because she has swollen feet.

How are the feet?

She says they are still giving her trouble. I ask Chimane, How are your people at Nokaneng? They have not written?

She shook her head.

I could see from her eyes that her mind was on another thing and not her people at that moment.

Wait for me Chimane eh, forgive me, I have scones in the oven, eh! I will just take them out and come back, eh!

When I came back to her Chimane was wiping her eyes. They were wet.

Karabo, you know what?

E — e. I shook my head.

I am heavy with child.

Hau!

There was a moment of silence.

Who is it, Chimane?

Timi. He came back only to give me this.

But he loves you. What does he say have you told him?

I told him yesterday. We met in town.

I remembered I had not seen her at the Black Crow.

Are you sure, Chimane? You have missed a month?

She nodded her head.

Timi himself — he did not use the thing?

I only saw after he finished, that he had not.

Why? What does he say?

He tells me he says I should not worry I can be his wife.

Timi is a good boy, Chimane. How many of these boys with town ways who know too much will even say Yes it is my child?

Hai, Karabo, you are telling me other things now. Do you not see that I have not worked long enough for my people? If I marry now who will look after them when I am the only child?

Hm. I hear your words. It is true. I tried to think

of something soothing to say.

Then I say You can talk it over with Timi. You can go home and when the child is born you look after it for three months and when you are married you come to town to work and can put your money together to help the old people while they are looking after the child.

What shall we be eating all the time I am at home? It is not like those days gone past when we had land and our mother could go to the fields until the child was ready to arrive.

The light goes out in my mind and I cannot think of the right answer. How many times have I feared the same thing! Luck and the mercy of the gods that is all I live by. That is all we live by — all of us.

Listen, Karabo. I must be going to make tea for Madam. It will soon strike half-past ten.

I went back to the house. As Madam was not in yet, I threw myself on the divan in the sitting-room. Malan came sniffing at my legs. I put my foot under its fat belly and shoved it up and away from me so that it cried *tjunk — tjunk — tjunk* as it went out. I say to it I say Go and tell your brother what I have done to you and tell him to try it and see what I will do. Tell your grandmother when she comes home too.

When I lifted my eyes he was standing in the kitchen door, Dick. He says to me he says *Hau!* now you have also begun to speak to dogs!

I did not reply. I just looked at him, his mouth ever stretched out like the mouth of a bag, and I passed to my room.

I sat on my bed and looked at my face in the mirror. Since the morning I had been feeling as if a black cloud were hanging over me, pressing on my head and shoulders. I do not know how long I sat there. Then I smelled Madam. What was it? Where was she? After a few moments I knew what it was. My perfume and scent. I used the same cosmetics as Mrs Plum's. I should have been used to it by now. But this morning — why did I smell Mrs Plum like this? Then, without knowing why, I asked myself I said, Why have I been using the same cosmetics as Madam? I wanted to throw them all out. I stopped. And then I took all the things and threw them into the dustbin. I was going to buy other kinds on Thursday; finished!

I could not sit down. I went out and into the white people's house. I walked through and the smell of the house made me sick and seemed to fill up my throat. I went to the bathroom without knowing why. It was full of the smell of Madam. Dick was cleaning the bath. I stood at the door and looked at him cleaning the dirt out of the bath, dirt from Madam's body. *Sies!* I said aloud. To myself I said, Why cannot people wash the dirt of their own bodies out of the bath? Before Dick knew I was near I went out. Ach, I said again to myself, why should I think about it now when I have been doing their washing for so long and cleaned the bath many times when Dick was ill. I had held worse things from her body times without number . . .

I went out and stood midway between the house and my room, looking into the next yard. The three-legged grey cat next door came to the fence and our eyes met. I do not know how long we stood like that looking at each other. I was thinking, Why don't you go and look at your grandmother like that, when it turned away and mewed hopping on the three legs. Just like someone who feels pity for you.

In my room I looked into the mirror on the chest

of drawers. I thought, is this Karabo this?

Thursday came, and the afternoon off. At the Black Crow I did not see Chimane. I wondered about her. In the evening I found a note under my door. It told me if Chimane was not back that evening I should know that she was at 660 3rd Avenue, Alexandra Township. I was not to tell the white people.

I asked Dick if he could not go to Alexandra with me after I had washed the dishes. At first he was unwilling. But I said to him I said, Chimane will not believe that you refused to come with me when she sees me alone. He agreed.

On the bus Dick told me much about his younger sister whom he was helping with money to stay at school until she finished, so that she could become a nurse and a midwife. He was very fond of her, as far as I could find out. He said he prayed always that he should not lose his job, as he had done many times before, after staying a few weeks only at each job; because of this he had to borrow money from people to pay his sister's school fees, to buy her clothes and books. He spoke of her as if she were his sweetheart. She was clever at school, pretty (she was this in the photo Dick had shown me before). She was in Orlando Township. She looked after his old people, although she was only thirteen years of age. He said to me he said Today I still owe many people because I keep losing my job. You must try to stay with Mrs Plum, I said.

I cannot say that I had all my mind on what Dick was telling me. I was thinking of Chimane: what could she be doing? Why that note?

We found her in bed. In that terrible township where night and day are full of knives and bicycle

chains and guns and the barking of hungry dogs and
of people in trouble. I held my heart in my hands.
She was in pain and her face, even in the candlelight,
was grey. She turned her eyes on me. A fat woman
was sitting in a chair. One arm rested on the other
and held her chin in its palm. She had hardly opened
the door for us after we had shouted our names when
she was on her bench again as if there were nothing
else to do.

She snorted, as if to let us know that she was going
to speak. She said There is your friend. There she is
my own-own niece who comes from the womb of my
sister, my sister who was make to spit out my
mother's breast to give way for me. Why does she go
and do such an evil thing. *Ao!* you young girls of
today you do not know children die so fast these
days that you have to thank God for sowing a seed in
your womb to grow into a child. If she had let the
child be born I should have looked after it or my
sister would have been so happy to hold a grandchild
on her lap, but what does it help? She has allowed a
worm to cut the roots, I don't know.

Then I saw that Chimane's aunt was crying. Not
once did she mention her niece by her name, so sore
her heart must have been. Chimane only moaned.

Her aunt continued to talk, as if she was never
going to stop for breath, until her voice seemed to
move behind me, not one of the things I was
thinking: trying to remember signs, however small,
that could tell me more about this moment in a dim
little room in a cruel township without street lights,
near Chimane. Then I remembered the three-legged
cat, its grey-green eyes, its *miau*. What was this
shadow that seemed to walk about us but was not
coming right in front of us?

I thanked the gods when Chimane came to work at the end of the week. She still looked weak, but that shadow was no longer there. I wondered Chimane had never told me about her aunt before. Even now I did not ask her.

I told her I told her white people that she was ill and had been fetched to Nokaneng by a brother. They would never try to find out. They seldom did, these people. Give them any lie, and it will do. For they seldom believe you whatever you say. And how can a black person work for white people and be afraid to tell them lies. They are always asking the questions, you are always the one to give the answers.

Chimane told me all about it. She had gone to a woman who did these things. Her way was to hold a sharp needle, cover the point with the finger, and guide it into the womb. She then fumbled in the womb until she found the egg and then pierced it. She gave you something to ease the bleeding. But the pain, spirits of our forefathers!

Mrs Plum and Kate were talking about dogs one evening at dinner. Every time I brought something to table I tried to catch their words. Kate seemed to find it funny, because she laughed aloud. There was a word I could not hear well which began with *sem* —: whatever it was, it was to be for dogs. This I understood by putting a few words together. Mrs Plum said it was something that was common in the big cities of America, like New York. It was also something Mrs Plum wanted and Kate laughed at the thought. Then later I was to hear that Monty and Malan could be sure of a nice burial.

Chimane's voice came up to me in my room the next morning, across the fence. When I come out she tells me she says *Hei* child-of-my-father, here is some-

thing to tickle your ears. You know what? What? I
say. She says, These white people can do things that
make the gods angry. More godless people I have not
seen. The madam of our house says the people of
Greenside want to buy ground where they can bury
their dogs. I heard them talk about it in the sitting
room when I was giving them coffee last night. *Hei*,
people, let our forefathers come and save us!

Yes, I say, I also heard the madam of our house
talk about it with her daughter. I just heard it in
pieces. By my mother one day these dogs will sit at
table and use knife and fork. These things are to be
treated like people now, like children who are never
going to grow up.

Chimane sighed and she says *Hela batho,* why do
they not give me some of that money they will spend
on the ground and on gravestones to buy stockings! I
have nothing to put on, by my mother.

Over her shoulder I saw the cat with three legs. I
pointed with my head. When Chimane looked back
and saw it she said *Hm,* even *they* live like kings. The
mother-in-law found it on a chair and the madam said
the woman should not drive it away. And there was
no other chair, so the woman went to her room.

Hela!

I was going to leave when I remembered what I
wanted to tell Chimane. It was that five of us had
collected £1 each to lend her so that she could pay
the woman of Alexandra for having done that thing
for her. When Chimane's time came to receive money
we collected each month and which we took in turns,
she would pay us back. We were ten women and each
gave £2 at a time. So one waited ten months to
receive £20. Chimane thanked us for helping her.

I went to wake up Mrs Plum as she had asked me.

She was sleeping late this morning. I was going to knock at the door when I hard strange noises in the bedroom. What is the matter with Mrs Plum, I asked myself. Should I call her, in case she is ill? No, the noises were not those of a sick person. They were happy noises but like those a person makes in a dream, the voice full of sleep. I bent a little to peep through the keyhole. What is this? I kept asking myself. Mrs Plum! Malan! What is she doing this one? Her arm was round Malan's belly and pressing its back against her stomach at the navel, Mrs Plum's body in a nightdress moving in jerks like someone in fits . . . her leg rising and falling . . . Malan silent like a thing to be owned without any choice it can make to belong to another.

The gods save me, I heard myself saying, the words sounding like wind rushing out of my mouth. So this is what Dick said I would find out for myself!

No one could say where it all started; who talked about it first; whether the police wanted to make a reason for taking people without passes and people living with servants and working in town or not working at all. But the story rushed through Johannesburg that servants were going to poison the white people's dogs. Because they were too much work for us: that was the reason. We heard that letters were sent to the newspapers by white people asking the police to watch over the dogs to stop any wicked things. Some said that we the servants were not really bad, we were being made to think of doing these things by evil people in town and in the locations. Others said the police should watch out lest we poison madams and masters because black people did not know right from wrong when they were angry. We were still children at heart, others said.

Mrs Plum said that she had also written to the papers.

Then it was the police came down on the suburbs like locusts on a cornfield. There were lines and lines of men who were arrested hour by hour in the day. They liked this very much, the police. Everybody they took, everybody who was working was asked, Where's the poison eh? Where did you hide it? Who told you to poison the dogs eh? If you tell us we'll leave you to go free, you hear? And so many other things.

Dick kept saying It is wrong this thing they want to do to kill poor dogs. What have these things of God done to be killed for? Is it the dogs that make us carry passes? Is it dogs that make the laws that give us pain? People are just mad they do not know what they want, stupid! But when white policemen spoke to him, Dick trembled and lost his tongue and the things he thought. He just shook his head. A few moments after they had gone through his pockets he still held his arms stretched out, like the man of straw who frightens away birds in a field. Only when I hissed and gave him a sign did he drop his arms. He rushed to a corner of the garden to go on with his work.

Mrs Plum had put Monty and Malan in the sitting room, next to her. She looked very much worried. She called me. She asked me she said Karabo, you think Dick is a boy we can trust? I did not know how to answer. I did not know whom she was talking about when she said *we*. Then I said I do not know, Madam. You know, she said. I looked at her. I said I do not know what Madam thinks. She said she did not think anything, that was why she asked. I nearly laughed because she was telling a lie this time and not I.

At another time I should have been angry if she lied to me, perhaps. She and I often told each other lies, as Kate and I also did. Like when she came back from jail, after that day when she turned a hosepipe on two policemen. She said life had been good in jail. And yet I could see she was ashamed to have been there. Not like our black people who are always being put in jail and only look at it as the white man's evil game. Lilian Ngoyi often told us this, and Mrs Plum showed me how true those words are. I am sure that we have kept to each other by lying to each other.

There was something in Mrs Plum's face as she was speaking which made me fear her and pity her at the same time. I had seen her when she had come from prison; I had seen her when she was shouting at Kate and the girl left the house; now there was this thing about dog poisoning. But never had I seen her face like this before. The eyes, the nostrils, the lips, the teeth seemed to be full of hate, tired, fixed on doing something bad; and yet there was something on that face that told me she wanted me on her side.

Dick is all right madam, I found myself saying. She took Malan and Monty in her arms and pressed them to herself, running her hands over their heads. They looked so safe, like a child in a mother's arms.

Mrs Plum said All right you may go. She said Do not tell anybody what I have asked about Dick eh?

When I told Dick about it, he seemed worried.

It is nothing, I told him.

I had been thinking before that I did not stand with those who wanted to poison the dogs, Dick said. But the police have come out, I do not care what happens to the dumb things, now.

I asked him I said Would you poison them if you were told by someone to do it?

No. But I do not care, he replied.

The police came again and again. They were having a good holiday, everyone could see that. A day later Mrs Plum told Dick to go because she would not need his work any more.

Dick was almost crying when he left. Is madam so unsure of me, he asked. I never thought a white person could fear me! And he left.

Chimane shouted from the other yard. She said, *Hei ngoana'rona,* the boers are fire-hot eh!

Mrs Plum said she would hire a man after the trouble was over.

A letter came from my parents in Phokeng. In it they told me my uncle had passed away. He was my mother's brother. The letter also told me of other deaths. They said I would not remember some, I was sure to know the others. There were also names of sick people.

I went to Mrs Plum to ask her if I could go home. She asks she says When did he die? I answer I say It is three days, madam. She says So that they have buried him? I reply Yes Madam. Why do you want to go home then? Because my uncle loved me very much madam. But what are you going to do there? To take my tears and words of grief to his grave and to my aunt, madam. No you cannot go, Karabo. You are working for me you know? Yes, madam. I, and not your people pay you. I must go madam, that is how we do it among my people, madam. She paused. She walked into the kitchen and came out again. If you want to go, Karabo, you must lose the money for the days you will be away. Lose my pay, madam? Yes, Karabo.

The next day I went to Mrs Plum and told her I was leaving for Phokeng and was not coming back to

her. Could she give me a letter to say that I worked
for her. She did, with her lips shut tight. I could feel
that something between us was burning like raw
chillies. The letter simply said that I had worked for
Mrs Plum for three years. Nothing more. The memory
of Dick being sent away was still an open sore in my
heart.

The night before the day I left, Chimane came to
see me in my room. She had her own story to tell me.
Timi, her boyfriend, had left her — for good. Why?
Because I killed his baby. Had he not agreed that you
should do it? No. Did he show he was worried when
you told him you were heavy? He was worried, like
me as you saw me, Karabo. Now he says if I kill one I
shall eat all his children up when we are married. You
think he means what he says? Yes, Karabo. He says
his parents would have been very happy to know that
the woman he was going to marry can make his seed
grow.

Chimane was crying, softly.

I tried to speak to her, to tell her that if Timi left
her just like that, he had not wanted to marry her in
the first place. But I could not, no, I could not. All I
could say was do not cry, my sister, do not cry. I gave
her my handkerchief.

Kate came back the morning I was leaving, from
somewhere very far I cannot remember where. Her
mother took no notice of what Kate said asking her
to keep me, and I was not interested either.

One hour later I was on the Railway bus to
Phokeng. During the early part of the journey I did
not feel anything about the Greenside house I had
worked in. I was not really myself, my thoughts
dancing between Mrs Plum, my uncle, my parents,
and Phokeng, my home. I slept and woke up many

times during the bus ride. Right through the ride I seemed to see, sometimes in sleep, sometimes between sleep and waking, a red car passing our bus, then running behind us. Each time I looked out it was not there.

Dreams came and passed. He tells me he says You have killed my seed I wanted my mother to know you are a woman in whom my seed can grow . . . Before you make the police take you to jail make sure that it is for something big you should go to jail for, otherwise you will come out with a heart and mind that will bleed inside you and poison you . . .

The bus stopped for a short while, which made me wake up.

The Black Crow, the club women . . . *Hei*, listen! I lie to the madam of our house and I say I had a telegram from my mother telling me she is very very sick. I show her a telegram my sister sent me as if mother were writing. So I went home for a nice weekend . . .

The laughter of the women woke me up, just in time for me to stop a line of saliva coming out over my lower lip. The bus was making plenty of dust now as it was running over part of the road they were digging up. I was sure the red car was just behind us, but it was not there when I woke.

Any one of you here who wants to be baptized or has a relative without a church who needs to be can come and see me in the office . . . A round man with a fat tummy and sharp hungry eyes, a smile that goes a long, long way . . .

The bus was going uphill, heavily and noisily.

I kick a white man's dog, me, or throw it there if it has not been told the black people's law . . . This is Mister Monty and this is Mister Malan. Now get up you lazy boys and meet Mister Kate. Hold out your hands and say hello to him . . . Karabo, bring two glasses there . . . Wait a bit — What will you chew boys while Mister Kate and I have a drink? Nothing? Sure?

We were now going nicely on a straight tarred road and the trees rushed back. Mister Kate. What nonsense, I thought.

Look Karabo, madam's dogs are dead. What? Poison. I killed them. She drove me out of a job did she not? For nothing. Now I want her to feel she drove me out for something. I came back when you were in your room and took the things that poisoned them . . . And you know what? She has buried them in clean pink sheets in the garden. *Ao*, clean clean good sheets. I am going to dig them out and take one sheet do you want the other one? Yes, give me the other one I will send it to my mother . . . *Hei*, Karabo, see here they come. Monty and Malan. The bloody fools they do not want to stay in their hole. Go back you silly fools. Oh you do not want to move eh? Come here, now I am going to throw you in the big pool. No, Dick! No Dick! No, No! Dick! They cannot speak do not kill things that cannot speak. Madam can speak for them she always does. No! Dick . . .

I woke up with a jump after I had screamed Dick's name, almost hitting the window. My forehead was full of sweat. The red car also shot out of my sleep and was gone. I remembered a friend of ours who told us how she and the garden man had saved two white sheets in which their white master had buried their two dogs. They went to throw the dogs in a dam.

When I told my parents my story Father says to

me he says, So long as you are in good health my
child, it is good. The worker dies, work does not.
There is always work. I know when I was a boy a
strong sound body and a good mind were the biggest
things in life. Work was always there, and the lazy
man could never say there was no work. But today
people see work as something bigger than everything
else, bigger than health, because of money.

I reply I say, Those days are gone Papa. I must go
back to the city after resting a little to look for work.
I must look after you. Today people are too poor to
be able to help you.

I knew when I left Greenside that I was going to
return to Johannesburg to work. Money was little,
but life was full and it was better than sitting in
Phokeng and watching the sun rise and set. So I told
Chimane to keep her eyes and ears open for a job.

I had been at Phokeng for one week when a red car
arrived. Somebody was sitting in front with the
driver, a white woman. At once I knew it to be that
of Mrs Plum. The man sitting beside her was showing
her the way, for he pointed towards our house in
front of which I was sitting. My heart missed a few
beats. Both came out of the car. The white woman
said 'Thank you' to the man after he had spoken a
few words to me.

I did not know what to do and how to look at her
as she spoke to me. So I looked at the piece of cloth I
was sewing pictures on. There was a tired but soft
smile on her face. Then I remembered that she might
want to sit. I went inside to fetch a low bench for
her. When I remembered it afterwards, the thought
came to me that there are things I never think white
people can want to do at our homes when they visit
for the first time: like sitting, drinking water or

entering the house. This is how I thought when the white priest came to see us. One year at Easter Kate drove me home as she was going to the north. In the same way I was at a loss what to do for a few minutes.

Then Mrs Plum says, I have come to ask you to come back to me, Karabo. Would you like to?

I say I do not know, I must think about it first.

She says, Can you think about it today? I can sleep at the town hotel and come back tomorrow morning, and if you want to you can return with me.

I wanted her to say she was sorry to have sent me away, I did not know how to make her say it because I know white people find it too much for them to say sorry to a black person. As she was not saying it, I thought of two things to make it hard for her to get me back and maybe even lose me in the end.

I say, You must ask my father first, I do not know, should I call him?

Mrs Plum says, Yes.

I fetched both father and mother. They greeted her while I brought benches. Then I told them what she wanted.

Father asks mother and mother asks Father. Father asks me. I say if they agree, I will think about it and tell her the next day.

Father says, It goes by what you feel my child.

I tell Mrs Plum I say, If you want me to think about it I must know if you will want to put my wages up from £6 because it is too little.

She asks me, How much will you want?

Up by £4.

She looked down for a few moments.

And then I want two weeks at Easter and not just the weekend. I thought if she really wanted me she

would want to pay for it. This would also show how
sorry she was to lose me.

Mrs Plum says, I can give you one week. You see
you already have something like a rest when I am in
Durban in the winter.

I tell her I say I shall think about it.

She left.

The next day she found me packed and ready to
return with her. She was very much pleased and
looked kinder than I had ever known her. And me, I
felt sure of myself, more than I had ever done.

Mrs Plum says to me, You will not find Monty and
Malan.

Oh?

Yes, they were stolen the day after you left. The
police have not found them yet. I think they are dead
myself.

I thought of Dick . . . my dream. Could he? And
she . . . . did this woman come to ask me to return
because she had lost two animals she loved?

Mrs Plum says to me she says, You know, I like
your people, Karabo, the Africans.

And Dick and me, I wondered.

Introduction to the Poems

Nigeria. Blazing suns. Warm rains. Work from early morning to 2 pm for schools and offices. Lazy afternoons. Drink a cold lager. Just let perspiration ooze and run. Switch off from the outside world. Stretch yourself under the fan. Drop into a sensuous numbness, a delicious languor. Sleep. Wake up to evenings teeming with humanity. See crowds pouring into the market place studded with myriad candle lights. Listen to a variety of languages at the market, where people come to buy, court, exchange news and stories. High-life music always pushing against night from storefront radios and open-air night clubs . . . That's Lagos. That's Ibadan. That's any city in Nigeria.

Lagos is as south as you can go. South of the south is — could be anywhere south of the Equator. But at this time we are talking about the painful south, aren't we? Southern Africa. Further into the Nigerian hinterland is Ibadan. Further still is the real north, silently slipping under desert sand, Sahara. Vast savannah. Vast silences. Part of a bed laid out for the

Sahara to stretch full-length on its belly from the Atlantic to the Red Sea.

You are giving university lessons to adults here. So you move from one station to another every week in cycles and cycles of barren mile upon barren mile of road. But always, either side of you, is the vast savannah. It does not threaten to close you in like the lush rain forest of the southern coastal strip. So you fancy you can take liberties with it. December to March is the time of the harmattan. A dry wind that blows south from the Sahara, loaded with fine dust. The dusty haze stays on night and day, gradually petering in intensity, its scouring mischief almost spent by the time Lagos feels the presence of the season.

Exile in Nigeria [1]
1960

Northern Wind
sweeping down from the Sahara
flings a grey scarf round me on and off.
The car torpedoes through the smoky haze:
I wonder what you do to my interior —
burning dry the mucus
piercing
scouring
my lungs —
savage harmattan! [2]

Northern Wind
filtering
through tree and grass and me,
you hear my windows open
with a creak of hinges —
windows that were shut so long,
oh, so long
in the painful south of the south, [3]
and you laugh at me —
rollicking harmattan!

Northern Wind
smelling of what I cannot smell
reminding me of things I can't or daren't remember,
what is it you do to me?
If it's remaining embers your
wasted fingers
fumble for
or violence you're whipping me into,
groping
among slumbering drives of long ago down
in the cellar of the brain —
ah, save your breath;
I feel a certain void
now my enemies are out of sight;
only distant sound of long-tongued hounds
I hear
across the Congo and Zambesi and Limpopo
down in the painful south of the south,
and my anger
is a sediment
in the pit of my stomach
waiting
for Time's purgative or agitation —
harrowing harmattan!

Northern wind
all I know
is that you numb and jolt me
lash the water off my flesh
and fill me with a sense of insufficiency,
vague longings and forlorn moments and
brittle promises — maddening!
Twelve months I heard of you
there in the humid side of your native sands
where heat

oozed
from under me,
denuded
some of the lump of southern pain:
you did not come
I came so far to meet you.
Yesterday I watched the leaves
go fluttering
down
down
to kiss the ground before your majesty —
pretentious thing!

Northern wind
now whimpering
whining
now lisping
dead prophecies
collected from ruins of lost empires,[4]
you weave
knotted fingers
through tree and grass and me
blowing down the serest:
stop,
tremble
when you see the savage green of us
beyond the touch of you!
Not like the lusty August winds
of the vibrant painful south of the south,
spinning us into
desperate tears and laughter
anger, hope —
blistering interlace —
still pushing us on to hell or heaven,
we running fighting running,

straining
like a universe of bending reeds.
Rather that,
northern wind,
than the long hours of sleep,
oh, so long,
that make a yawning descant
to your impotent howling,
the long mental sleep
that knows no longing
for even the now unattainable,
no unfulfilled urges
heartburns and lingering angers,
no fires kindled by wanton men
beaten out
in psychotic panic
left smouldering smouldering smouldering
in the Negro heart
in the agitated painful south of the south.
When will you stifle
this yawn of ancient languors
in the range of your compass —
indifferent harmattan?

Northern wind
while I've been talking
I've become aware of one thing
I had only surmised
since I left the palpitating painful south of the south
they've done it to me —
taught me the violence,
revenge of Europe,
uncivilized me
by the law of
paper

gun
baton,
made me lie to them and smile,
made me think that
anger and bitterness
and running fighting running
were man's vital accessories.
Now here I fume and dig and paw the earth,
bellow
poised panting like a bull for the encounter and —
ah, no visible foe,
resistance none,
no dazzling red;
Ah the aching void in me,
neutralized acidity of my slime!
Now you know
the unsteady fulcrum of an immigrant!
Tell me,
is this divine indolence —
this
the horizontal sleep of the north?
the secret of the urge to be
only to be?
or just the great immensity of Northern Sleep?
Is it Tao's sweet narcotic wisdom —
spirit of harmattan?[5]

Northern wind
you know nothing.
Only, since morning
I've ridden layer after layer of grey
my nose is dry
your load trapped in my hair.
You've followed me all day
relentlessly

into the catacomb of night
and still I feel
the unholy hounds of the
bleeding painful south of the south
chasing after me,
you flapping about my head
gyrating like a pack of idiots
in and out between the running wheels —
Enough!
I shan't be wooed:
Shelley's long long dead,[6]
no messages thrown to the winds anymore
Enough
of dehydrated kisses,
barren maid,
no nightclub this!
But now I think of it
I'll stop at the roadhouse here
for a beer
just for a while —
the immigrant's journey's a long long one,
heavy.
He tunnels through
back again
beneath
pounding footsteps of three decades and more of
    hurt[7]
on the beaten road above
weighing down
down on him.
When I burst into the dawn of brooding questions
I shall yet look at more butterflies, moths and leaves
you nailed
on my radiator
like a lover of curios who wants his pieces

dead and flat.
Morning!
New dawn tells me
that void can never last,
for the immigrant's journey's a long long road.
Over centuries
they scrambled[8]
for my mother
from across the frontiers of snowbound boredom
decay
stale wines and bodies,
clawed down her green loveliness
mauled her limbs
sold her shrines
planted
brass and wooden crosses
knocked them down at skittles
gaming for the land
while hungry eyes transfixed on a miracle
high on Calvary.
I'm a leopard
born of
a Mother
a God in torment,
converging point of centuries of change,
a continent of test-tubes.[9]
My claws have poison:
only let me lie down a while,
bide my time,
rub my neck and whiskers,
file my claws and remember.
Then my mind can draw the line between
the hounds and hunted of the lot
in the blazing painful south of the south;
use their tools and brains —

thanks for once to ways of white folk.
And in yonder land of peace and calm,
you think I'll change my spots?
No matter,
no regrets.
Meantime,
let them leave my heart alone!

FOOTNOTES:

1.   On 6 September 1957 the author left South Africa to
      teach in Nigeria, where he lived for four years. Three of
      these were spent teaching university courses for adult
      classes under the University of Ibadan. This he did in the
      north, visiting four stations each week. The poem was
      written in the north.
2.   The wind. — See introduction to this poem.
3.   Southern Africa, which is south of Lagos.
4.   The great empires of Ghana, Mali and Songhai which
      flourished about 700 — 1600 AD.
5.   Tao: *The Book of Tao* (translated by Lin Yutang,
      London, Michael Joseph 1944), written by Laotse, the
      ancient Chinese philosopher (born c. 570 BC), contains
      a doctrine that teaches the importance of inaction,
      better interpreted from Chinese as 'non-interference'.
      Let things ride, so to speak; approach life with humility,
      quietude, calm, rather than force, pride, self-assertion.
      This views man as part of the whole rhythm of life.
      Some of the paradoxes in *The Book of Tao* are: that the
      cleverest man behaves as if he were stupid; the man who
      stutters can actually be the most eloquent; the more

obsessed one is with knowledge, the less one gets to know; there is no beauty in victory, and the person who gets excited about victory must love killing; a victory should be celebrated with a funeral ceremony; love is a good defence against destruction; the man who gives to other people has greater abundance, etc. But the author of this poem did not mean to suggest Taoism in depth. He was commenting on appearances. The relatively slower pace of life in northern Nigeria and the simple ascetic form of worship in the mosques, the vast silences of the savannah, brought to his mind the teachings of Tao. Could it be that these teachings are a drug (narcotic) under the influence of which the believer is inactive, need neither resist outwardly nor attack, but that there is wisdom underneath this show of calm? Appearances and actualities . . . In September and October of 1966 the Northerners began a large-scale slaughter of the Ibos who lived and worked among them, and whom they considered as treacherous aliens associated with the earlier deaths of northern leaders in the Federal government. China itself as a united nation does not today appear as anything that Tao would have approved.

6.   In his 'Ode to the West Wind' Percy Bysshe Shelley (1792 – 1822) pleads to the autumn wind to listen to him because something sad is weighing down on him. He is asking the wind to sing through him, the way a string instrument will vibrate, so that the wind may in turn carry the poet's message to mankind. Poets today do not speak to the elements in the manner Shelley and his contemporaries used to do.

7.   The writer was 37 when he left South Africa for Nigeria.

8.   Refers to the scramble for Africa by European powers who divided the continent among themselves in 1885 in the process of colonizing it.

9. Refers to a continent where Europeans have carried out several experiments in capitalism and slavery, Christianity, Islam, archeology etc.

Death

You want to know?
My mother died at 45
at 42 my brother followed.
You want to know?
She cleaned the houses of white folk,
and washed their bodily dirt
out of the baths.
One night a coma took her,
and he —
cancer hounded him two years
and rolled him in the dust.
You want to know?
My grandma left at 80,
she also washed her years away
and saw them flow
into the drain
with the white man's scum.
Many more from our tree have fallen —
known and unknown.

    . . . and that white colossus

he was butchered by a man
they say is mad.

How often do I dream
my dearest dead stand across a river —
small and still I cannot traverse
to join them
and I try to call to them
and they wave and smile so distantly
receding beyond the water
that pulls me in
and spits me out into the dawn of the living.

. . . and he was butchered
like a buffalo
after overseeing many a negro's execution.

You want to know —
why do I say all this?
what have they to do with us
the ones across the water?
How should I know?
These past two decades
death has been circling closer
and beating the air about me
like a flight of vultures
in a cruel age
when instruments of torture
can be found with any fool and tyrant,
churchman, all alike,
all out to tame the heretic, they say.

. . . and they tell us
when the colossus fell
he did not even have a triple-worded

Roman chance[1]

And so to kill a bug
they set a house on fire
to kill a fire
they flood a country
to save a country
drench the land in blood
to peg the frontiers of their colour madness
they'll herd us into ghettoes
jail us
kill us slowly
because we are the Attribute
that haunts their dreams
because *they* are the blazing neon lights
that will not let us be
because we are the children of their Sin
they'll try to erase the evidence
because their deeds are howling from a fog
beyond their reach.

. . . and we laughed and danced
when news came of the death of that colossus
— the death of a beast of prey.

What can we do with the ashes of a tyrant?
who will atone?
whose blood will pay for those of us who went
down under the tanks of fire?
And voices cried It's not enough,
a tyrant dead is not enough!
Vengeance is mine and yours and his,
says the testament of man
nailed to the boulder of pain.

. . . and they say the butcher's mad
who sank the knife into the tyrant's neck
while the honourable men
who rode his tanks of fire
looked on
as if they never heard of giants die
as they had lived,
and all about the frog who burst
when he pushed his energy
beyond the seams of his own belly.

What if I go as the unknown soldier
or attended by a buzzing fly?
what if my carcass were soaked in organ music,
or my ancestors had borne me home?
I hear already
echoes from a future time of voices
coming from a wounded bellowing multitude
cry Who will atone
Who will atone?

You want to know? —
because I nourish
a deadly life within
my madness shall have blood.

Denver, Colorado.

FOOTNOTE:

'A triple-worded Roman chance' refers to Julius Caesar's
last words: 'Et tu, Brute'.

Somewhere

Somewhere a mother sobs
through bomb-shattered nights
hunger drains the blood of children.
Somewhere we eat the sputum of our pride
when we know nothing and we blunder.
Somewhere a woman sees her sick man
teeter on the edge of midnight
and turn his back to her and all forever.
Somewhere in the arena we lose our heads
amid the boos and jeers and whoops
along the sidelines.
Somewhere a mother waits
her man, her son
in chains of an oppressor
or waits for those who never come
and still endures we know not how.
And yet amid the smoking debris
of a fear-driven world
while man juggles with megaton eggs,
somewhere a woman gives the world an artist:
a child who sings and dances,

dreams and weaves a poem round the universe
plunging down the womb
to fire a cell
sinking down a borehole
to probe the spring of life
from where the earth will rise
to meet the sky.
Somewhere in ancient China, it is told,
a man made a song
out of the wailing of a dove
a song that moved all animals
to rise and kill the serpent
who ate the bird's young ones.
To know our sorrow
is to know our joy —
somewhere a mother will rejoice.

                                        Denver, Colorado.

Homeward Bound

The mountains that I like
and do not fear
don't stoop over me
like giant apes marooned
on a patch of Time;

they are the forms beyond,
holding down
the edge of blue
and etching with a light
of ever-changing tints;

— they can look the way I want them.

I do not like the lights
that come at me
and stab and flail
and blind the eyes of night
that bounce and cling on tarmac;

those shimmering faraway bodies

softly throbbing
tell me and love
that coffee's on the boil
she's listening for my footsteps;

— they can look the way I want them.

But you beside me here —
the contours of
your mountainscape
lead me to sniff at the corners
of your passion and sprawl
in the light and shade of your valleys
reminding me clearly
distant sights
can easily become
explosions of a mood;

so let us ride along
through dewy midnights
dewy dawns
and tumble gently into
disembowelled noontides;

— you need not look just the way I want.

Denver, Colorado.

AUTHOR'S NOTE:

Savannah, the plains, that's my kind of territory. Not high
mountains. Losing livestock as a herdboy; having to sleep in

the mountains for fear of a beating; taken out at night to the mountains by the bigger boys to hunt rock rabbits — a test of male toughness — those were the fears of part of my childhood. This inland animal also finds the sea boring when it's not menacing.

Death II

When you fear the day when you'll be old
here where voices knock about in tincans
or burst in passions
    black
        white and beige,
where youth will trample down the old and rock
and roll
    jive away
        or leave them
shaking in their holes
grounded by the pack
that now are breathing scratching on the door,

then
    drip
        drop
            drip
something trickles from
your ego centre
sinister
like water

dripping
    from a pipe within a wall
    out of reach.

When you fear the time you'll age or die
tonight
    tomorrow
        any day or night,
before you've gathered all your harvest
from that crazy brain
before you've told the story —
everything
about the muscle apes
who ride their tanks of fire
dealing death
holding birth in ambush
so you want to howl
    howl
        howl into the night
from hill to hill
where ancestors commune
for all who care to hear their beat —
yes you want
to tell it all
in many many words
like the dotty traveller
whose eyes are burning with the message.
Then more than ever
you must know
that words are like a tumour:
bleed them
    let them chafe and sweat
    and beat against the bone
    until the hour of dawn
    delivers you.

When you fear the day you'll die,
these days
when high or low romance
is black or white or beige —
a child of ethnic pain or glory —
rooms with rats and roaches
leaves a stink in government houses
kills and hangs for king and country
rides the word and song
of Billy Graham and Ethel Waters
pledging hallelujas shangri-las
and fiery chariots
(millions waiting to be fed and housed) —
come the never-never day
beyond millenium and beyond —

When you think of dying
and know you'll never know you're dead
you won't be there when they arrive
and shake three hundred years of dust
from out their lives,
and this may be
when you begin your endless night,
you won't be there to love and hate
or feel a woman's love and people's hate
to love and love and love
until it aches —
when you think all this
you coil around the ego centre
like the centipede the children tease,
then
    drip
        drop
           drip
something trickles from

the ego centre
sinister
like water
dripping
   from a pipe within a wall,
   out of reach.

You hunger for a feast of welcome
after all
the years of long and dizzy farewells.

Always you have known that
fame is offal to be tossed to mongrels;
events and times have nailed you
to the ego centre
all the years you've paced the wilderness
for some oasis,
nailed you so you could not break away
away and back to them who wait, endure.

Now's the time
for you to know
you still can grab
a few more years
hold on to them
for leverage
to make the jump
— perhaps the last —
claw the air
to mountain top
and scream and holler
from the bowels
of your ego
scream and holler
so they hear

their native son
remember you —
assure you that
you're fool to think
that fifty-five
has thrown you out
upon the cold
and salty shore
and this wide world
to pass you by —
assure you that
there will be time
for you to flee
the drooling years
among the strangers,
time enough
to drink with peers
you left behind
tell each other
how it's been
in your two worlds
time enough
to talk and listen
with the youth,
weep to ponder
friendships dead
and buried under
mounds of sand
just deep enough
to show you rags
in mute reproach —
assure you that
before that day
there's time to gather
up the cargo

of your mind
to show the folks,
although your words
may splutter cold
against the foggy
night between us,
though simple logic
resolution
walk on crutches
still you've got
to sing and shout
and they'll be listening
   . . . be listening
    . . . listening.

and still
  drip
    drop
      drip
something trickles from
your ego centre
sinister like water
dripping
  from a pipe within a wall
  out of reach . . .

FOOTNOTE:

The theme is from the sonnet by John Keats (1795 – 1821),
'When I have fears that I may cease to be', written three years
before his death. Keats was always haunted by visions of great
poets from the past, e.g. Edmund Spenser, Shakespeare,

Milton. These visions never left him, we are told. His first book
of poems (1817) was published when he was 22. He was
sickly, a victim of tuberculosis, and feared to die in his youth.
Which would mean the end of an exciting life as a poet, the
end of an adventure — that of exploring the mysteries, the
romance, the beauties, the truths of bygone ages and of his
own time; it will be the end of loving and being loved, the end
of the possibility of fame. Love? Yes. Fame? The writer of
'Death II' thinks he can do without it. There are other things
that bother the present writer: (a) He may grow old in strange
lands outside Africa — USA for instance, where elderly folk
are shoved away, often by their own blood relations, in
nursing homes; where old people live in constant fear of
assault, robbery in their own apartments; where they are
lonely, written off by society. The cult of youth in the USA is
frightening: millions of dollars are spent every day advertising
chemical preparations and clothing aimed at preserving youth;
(b) He may die in exile, never hear his people or be read or
heard by them. Africans do not want to die just anywhere.
They want to be buried in their own country. The poet wants
to return, to snatch the few years he may still have left, and
live them passionately, among his folk. The thought of
missing, as it were, that last boat or flight back home — *that's*
what makes him feel as if he were bleeding from the very
centre of his being. An idea that comes from the Sotho
expression, 'pelo e rotha madi' — blood dripping from the
heart; not quite the same as 'my heart bleeds'; (c) He will
never be able to give expression to the many things that are
burning inside him.

Vignettes

I

The thing we are talking about tonight is part of the great fight we are carrying on and it represents a forward and an upward look — a pushing onward. You and I have been breasting hills; we have been climbing upward; there has been progress and we can see it day by day looking back along blood-filled paths . . .

W.E.B. du Bois, *The Crisis,* October 1926.[1]

I wonder why those geese[2]
keep haunting me
daring me, it seems, to
make this poem.
I saw them
breasting the wind
across the slopes of greenery
one morning.
Stopped in my jogging tracks
and counted

I'd say at least
three score of them.

you and I have been breasting hills . . .

They flaunted patterns
of brown and black
and roan and white
and green,
walking on the slope
as if ahead
were bearers of a coffin,
or they were pickets
bent on raising hell for
bureaucrats
and telling them their goose was cooked
and they must deliver —
a purpose much much bigger
than the crumbs of bread
these numskulls
come and throw to them
over the fence.

you and I have been breasting hills . . .

Then it was I learned
   again
as I had done so many times
   that
nature can be mean or kind
   and elegant
for no other reason
than the dumb urge
to move from here
   to there.

I could myself
have been a goose
walking on a slope of greenery
drawn by the mute
togetherness and chaos of life:

haven't you and I been breasting hills? . . .

Then one night I dreamed
those geese were raising cackling hell
at the garment factory:
WE WANT MORE PAY AND BENEFITS!
Then the tanks came out and blew
the geese
   to feathereens,
insides flying all over the place . . .

you and I have been breasting hills . . .

Next day I went
once more
to the pond by the hill.
The geese were scattered
on the hillside
doing different things and nothings:
yes, so much for dreams!

I wonder why those geese
keep haunting me
daring me, it seems, to
make this poem.
Now it seems that
   beauty
will not last for its own sake.
Beauty only means the

parts are put together right
to shape the order that you want.

And when I see it,
it seems it can't be true
could *be* such order
as a flock of geese
walking across a hill of greenery
serene and breasting the wind.
And so the tanks of fire . . .
and up the thing will go in feathers!
You see,
they poisoned beauty for me
at the very source
in the painful south
except what we could salvage
from the tyranny of time and place
for ourselves and others:
and of course —

you and I have been breasting hills . . .

II

I see this prof
stomping up 34th
breasting the wind
and make a broadside
down Chestnutt,
mackintosh billowing behind him,
afro head thrown forward,
mouth open slightly,
and he stomps as if
to measure his father's land

and peg a claim.

I say to myself:
that prof has pantzer divisions
in his head,
    blueprints
of some deadly business
    in his bag
and somebody'll have
    to beware:
I know this because
    you and I have been breasting hills . . .

III

I see this dude —
six feet of elegance
    and style —
take his time
    down 34th:
capacious hat
throws
    a shade of subtle menace
over
    his quick-moving eyes:
a long grey coat
    with fringe of fur top and bottom
he casts
    a figure so delicate
the wind might break him.
But I watch him
    scrape the wind
with left hand
    like he's steering

body through a fissure in the wind,
   while weaving
bending away
   from its cutting edge.
The wind keeps coming on
   but he's breasting it:
been coming on long's
   he can remember.
No pantzer divisions
   in his head
no bag no blueprints:
   knows the art
     of feeling good and bad,
      of dying many times,
cutting corners cutting losses —
victories are so little
you must hug them
   feel them:
to pay your debts you've got forever.
And while he preens himself
   before the sidewalk window
they're on top of him —
   the minions of the law —
bung him into the car,
but not before he turns
   to look at me:
What do I see
   in that face but the
   landscape where
poetry and history
   make their concourse.
And I, sitting here tonight,
what do I know
   but that
the geese made fat by all the folks

who love only things that cannot talk —
those geese can only die
   in my poisoned dream;
   but that
the dude will live a people's poetry,
   their history;
   but that
the prof must go on stomping into
   fortresses
to stake our claim
and even sometimes beat them
   at their game
in the night of stratagems
in the open daylight of debate?
What do I know, I say,
   but that
you and I are always breasting hills?
Otherwise
   this poem must die and you the gods
will have to tell me something else tonight.

IV

Bra Moremi
comes up Newtown Street
heading for downtown Jo'burg,
swinging shoulder,
hands in pockets,
like litter in the streets
the reek of factory pork
and gingerbearded winos
could never touch him.

you and I have been breasting hills . . .

never mind:
*   ta-night is ta-night Missus Rosenbaum.*
Katusi sends his brothers off to school
*   this morning,*
Pa and Ma have gone to white man's town . . .
*   ta-night is ta-night Missus Rosenbaum,*
ta-night your jewels are mine.

Down Eloff Street
    he pushes through
the multi-coloured crowd
like there wasn't
    pinkies around
ready any time to kick
    shove him off
just to feel
    who they are.

You see him pushing south and then you know
he's staying on the line
they set for him —
the way those railway tracks
have pushed aside the bush
and thread their way
between the hills
tapering out in the distance
far's the eye can see,
dominant and lonely.

you and I have been breasting hills . . .

never mind:
*   ta-night is ta-night Missus Rosenbaum.*
Vukani's bathing grandpa's feet
*   this morning.*

Pa has followed Ma into the Night . . .
    ta-night is ta-night Missus Rosenbaum,
ta-night your jewels are mine.

Yesterday
    our fathers shook the earth
beneath their shoeless feet,
breasting hills and winds;
their song and shout
    flooded valleys,
brought the night tumbling down
    on laagered enemy;
Soon
    only the memory of song and shout and smoke
would hang over the trail
    of blood and debris.

Today
    this juba
has to push through crowds
    on enemy ground —
today
    when heroes are minted
in the braveries of prison islands,
hanging head down from a noose
    in the butcher's cold-cold cells,
done in by cops
    whose teeth were filed in their mother's womb;
today,
    when parliament is full of
rabid bats and hooded ghouls
and barricades itself with hounds and guns,
    out of reach
for messengers or plumbers, clerks or profs
    who only stomp and push their blackness

far as you can spit.

you and I have been breasting hills . . .

never mind:
*   ta-night is ta-night Missus Rosenbaum.*
He swore he'd never leave his big-eyed woman
*   yesterday night*
For Pa and Ma they went their separate ways . . .
*   ta-night is ta-night Missus Rosenbaum,*
ta-night your jewels are mine.

For three young men —
Moremi and Vukani and Katusi —
history began when they were born;
but their blood,
    their fathers' earth,
will always ring
    the Elders' song of bygone days that
— come renewal time —
    will sew together all the scattered epics
of our day.

He said for them to meet at Clarendon Circle . . . get
it together, Vukani! . . . bring the Rosenbaum pick-up
after pork deliveries
    . . . go on to Clarendon . . . Katusi'll bring the tools,
remember Clarendon Circle now . . . when the clock
strikes ten at the Greek man's corner . . . we move we
move to Rosenbaum . . . we'll take him one of his
pork sausages . . .

For *now*
    no elegance of geese
    no style of cadillac brothers

there across the seas;
but don't they say that and I and all
    from east to west
have all the years been breasting hills and winds
    the size of a whole black universe? —

never mind:
    for ta-night is ta-night Missus Rosenbaum, ta-night
your jewels are mine.

June, 1976

FOOTNOTES:

1.   W.E.B. du Bois, the Afro-American sociologist, thinker
     and man of letters. Born 1868 in Great Barrington,
     Massachusetts, died in 1963 in Ghana where he was
     directing work on *Encyclopaedia Africana.* He was
     buried in Ghana. Du Bois was one of the founders of the
     National Association for the Advancement of Coloured
     People (NAACP), and first editor of its journal, *The
     Crisis.*

2.   Author's comment: I was jogging one morning in Wayne,
     a village of greater Philadelphia. I saw a flock of geese
     walking on a lawn, beside a pond. Strange that geese
     should walk together like that, so many of them, as if
     they had a collective purpose somewhere out there
     ahead of them. For about six months those geese had me
     worried, as if they were urging me to write a poem about
     them. I would hear myself thinking aloud, asking them:
     what the devil can I say about you, just walking like
     that, like some dumb zombies? What's so special about

you anyway? They wouldn't leave me alone. I would dream about them. Then I saw two blacks walking, each in his own style and on different occasions — a professor and a swanky swaggering fellow obviously not the professor type. Things began to interconnect. But what was the meaning of these relationships? Come on you dumb beautiful geese, tell me . . .

Dedication to
Voices in the Whirlwind

FOR DENNIS BRUTUS:
    You stopped a fascist bullet.
FOR KGOSITSILE:
    Your 'borrowed fears'
    are also mine —
    and so your questionings.
FOR GWENDOLYN BROOKS:
    Thanks for the incisive image.
    You are a focus of
    the many streams of Black reality;
    Your heart straddles
    the times of unobtrusive grief
    to times of rage;
    rendering the drama
    you bring home the meaning.
FOR CHABI AND PUSO:
    My youngest two:
    the whirlwind's coming
    to meet you
    my sons.
    Don't ever let it hug you

twist you hurt you.
It's none too soon
to learn the signs:
see that bird over there
poised on a wingspan
to ride the storm —
the bride knows its enemies:
that's the abc of it,
sons.
It's never too soon.

A Prayer

Hear me son of the soil,
I have returned to this killing ground
the size and depth
of countless oceans of
Black anguish —
this killing ground,
these winter days of '76.

Nineteen years I've roamed the continents
renting one glasshouse after another
whence I've gazed and gazed
upon the wilderness of exile
all around me,
fearing rain and snow
because they shut me in,
busying myself, with others,
trying to pave the way for our return
and still turning around in circles,
sowing seed
on borrowed land
for crops we'll always have to leave behind,

kept alive only by
hope and faith,
by fellowship with other minds
that also chafe
against the heel of corporate power
holding this world to ransom.

Hear me son of the soil:
all these years I've heard the voices of my ancestors
calling
    calling
        calling
way across the seas
telling me,
    telling me
it's time to come home
    to come home.

The gates were opened
like they do in ancient allegory,
and here I am, son of the soil.
Amid the cheers and cries of welcome
I see the bloodhounds sniffing
on this killing ground,
    yelping,
        rooting
for another chase and still more blood.

Hear me son of the soil
when I say
I have returned
    to this killing ground
because I heard my ancestors calling.
Soweto's but an episode
    in our recital

of an epic of three hundred years.

I feel the earth flow through my fingers
    in Soweto,
and then down Second Avenue that is
    no more,
and then in the village
    of Maupaneng.
Here I knew that Time had buried
all the terrors of my childhood
underneath the sand and stones
that now have raised the floor
of what was once my reckless river,
    almost levelling it.
Auntie Dora was too sick and dazed
to care when she was told
her long-lost nephew was
but a few hours away,
she just didn't wait
    just couldn't.
I saw her dark little body in a box
where death had wrapped up
    all the fire and fury of her life.

Auntie Stina, she it was who held me tight
against her trembling body
that has stood the hammer and chisel
    of arthritis
half its five and eighty years.

Hear me tell you son of the soil:
I've reconnected and
    become renewed on this killing ground;
hear me when I say
it's a long long road for the exile:

I've tunnelled through
   back again
   beneath pounding footsteps of five decades
   bearing down on me,
because I must step forward
and be counted with the rest
whose lives derive their meaning from
the tyranny of place
   here on this killing ground,
here where the ancestors forever
   keep their vigil.
I know what they want of me
   from the start,
we'll work it out.
They're telling me
   that this is where it's got to be
on this killing ground.

Tomorrow I return to the glass house
   in the wilderness
that wants to suck me in,
   dissolve me.
Hear me son of the soil,
you haven't heard the last of us
   who want to be back in there
at this time of your resurgence
that you've earned so hard,
a few more hurdles now we'll be there —
   now,
not at some apocalyptic time —
the stuff that mystics peddle in —
   but now,
     and all the way.

Look once more son of the soil,

the killing ground is moist and ready
   for new seed.

Fathers and Sons

Fifteen years ago
they dragged me out at dawn
blindfolded me and shot me,
   then —
eternity wrapped me up
in my dazzling blackness.

Now you see
I have returned with others —
not like Lazarus
jolted from his grave,
maybe even grousing
that they yanked him out of sleep
that he so badly needed;
not like Lazarus
rubbing off the particles of sleep
and wobbling up the hill
to wait upon
the edge of the cliff
for a second going.

I come with fury
raising cyclones with my feet
and I have come to stay
come another dawn of firing squads.
Tell me not of second comings
or love of your god:
    I cannot feel it
    never have in all my terror-stricken years:
all I know
is that I'm 15 years of age
is that I feel the prison's cold and vermin
    crawling over me and nibbling on my heart
is that already I have seen the voltage
    in the fences of the law
is that I'm scared
because last night they buried many bodies
    in a big-big hole.
Tell my Mamma that I'm scared
hear me tell you that I'm scared
of them with hairy arms and yellow fingers
    shooting out like sausages.

Tell her that they asked me who's my father
and I said to them he's dead
and one of them had bluestone eyes
and ears like he was going to fly
and now I hear my Mamma's words about
a man they dragged outside at dawn
the sunset burning in his hooded eyes
and —
and now my heart is telling me —
that man with bluestone eyes
has *got* to have been there at dawn.

March 1977

A Poem

What is there that we can do or say
will sustain them
in those islands
where the sun was made for janitors?

What is there that we can say or do
will tear the years
from out the hands
of those who man the island galleys,

will bring them home and dry and mend them
bring them back
to celebrate
with us the song and dance and toil of living?

What is it that we must do or say
for children scattered
far from home
by hawks let loose to stay the judgment day?

The weeds run riot where our house is fallen

ourselves we roam
the wilderness.
'Go tell them there across the seas go tell him,'

so they say, 'his mother's dead six years,
he dare not come
he dare not write
the stars themselves have eyes and ears these days.'

You who fell before the cannon or
the sabered tooth
or lie on hallowed
ground: oh tell us what to say or do.

So many routes have led to exile since
your day our Elders
we've been here
and back in many cycles oh so many:

no terrain different drummers borrowed
dreams, and there
behind us now
the hounds have diamond fangs and paws of steel.

No time for dirge or burial without corpses:
teach us, Elders,
how to wait
and feel the centre, tame the time like masters,
sing the blues
so pain will bleed and let the islands in,
for exile is a ghetto of the mind.

To L S Senghor

I greet you, fellow-African,[1] on your seventieth birthday. It has been a long haul since Joal.[2] For so long too you've stomped up and down *le chemin de l'Europe, chemin de l'ambassade.*[3] Maybe longer than you care to remember. I greet you. You had a country to come back to. And you returned to lead a people that needed you, wanted you. They wrenched you from your moorings, you and your fellowmen, I mean those Frenchies. But they did not let you wander aimlessly on the seascape. They took you in hand. They gave you a language, you grabbed it and used it like a master. With it you made rhythms on the balafong[4] of your soul, its kora, its drums. You master of the grand gesture; of the grand resonance; of the grand Idea inflated with so many moments of feeling; sometimes emotion dripping schmaltz from the lush and grand Idea. Like in the 'New York' poem. It was somewhere else I found the power of your music, the real longings of your heart, the pain of your ecstasy, the ecstasy of your pain.

I myself have long since learned that word is rhythm, word is meaning rhythm and word and meaning and being are one. But I see only too well your dedication to poetry; am reminded always where we are with it when I read your meaning:

> With circumcision comes the end of childhood. Standing now at the roadside loaded with the trials of manhood you wish for that transparent night of innocence to return to. Ah, now you have to dance to conjure fears away, let the rhythm of the drum dispel your fear of manhood, let the childhood die in you. You need no words anymore for your poem, no form. Rhythm is all you need to build your manhood on, to define the poetry of transition. Life must be lived . . .

And so you must yourself feel the irony that lies in our love for the word, us children of black Africa, the poetry that rolls from the tongue with it all the time.

I greet you Senghor I greet you!

I met you first in *Chants d'Ombre.*[5] Nineteen years ago when I was still wondering how my mate and I had survived thirty-seven years of southern tremors and controls — a life which an artist could only discern in concrete minute-by-minute, day-by-day, responses. Responses that could best be captured through a racy breathless pressured diction. And here you came with the long musical line, with the grand aristocratic gesture. How could I but be either entranced or knocked off balance. First I tripped and fell and then I was enchanted. And then again when I heard that music in your lines, the voice of self-assurance, the measured pace of feeling rightly placed and pouring out in volumes I became impatient,

impatient because I loved my anger, loved my hatred. But always I learned what two different sets of white political values had done to you and me. No matter. I had already accepted the meeting point, the merging of the west and Africa in me down there in the painful temperate south. Yet something that I saw around me and read and listened to in the new Nigeria-Ghana terrain, your voice among them, did something to steady me, to measure the energy of Africa in me, the thing we had taken for granted in ghettos where you could never efface your blackness, where you've got to feel the tyranny of place and time. Even now I have not yet tamed the anger in me that never ceases to be touched off by the whirlwinds around me. Nor do I want to tame the bastard, lest I forget. I read your meaning:

> Let us listen to the voice of our forebears like Elissa out there in Portuguese Guinea where my folks came from. They were also exiles, like us, they would not choose to die and leave their seed behind to be swallowed up by the sands. Listen to the heart-warming spirits as they visit you in your hut; catch but a glimpse of them. Breathe the essence of the Dead even as you assemble and repeat their living words . . .

That is it you see. I've come full circle into the age-old theme of exile. Nineteen even ten years ago I still hoped for asylum in Africa, I did not yet perceive the poetry of exile. Reading you again it seems I'm hearing you for the first time. I listen also to another singer, Kofi's lines about lost souls lost souls lost souls who must return for purification. And something inside me leaps into a flame and tells me to be on the go again — this time, back to the tremors of

place and time. Only that will fortify the enclave of
my identity wherein sanity is secure. I read your
meaning:

> Time to leave. Unless you've come to stay, so that your
> roots sink deeper into alien ground here overseas, into
> this fertile soil, you've got to leave. Don't let the glitter
> of hotel suites keep you, or the screaming solitudes of
> city life. Time to go. Because already you hear the
> termites boring through your bones tearing down the
> youthfulness in your arms and legs. Time to leave. There
> won't be any friend to say goodbye at the station . . .

Jeunesse? Youth? Ah, that's anywhere along the
rugged road of commitment till it pitches you over
the cliff when it has no longer use of you.

I have been back these last few weeks for twenty-
one days there in the painful south. The brief
moment when the guards at the gate were called off.
In the wake of their power exercise you motored up
and down the cold cold killing ground of Soweto,
almost you could smell the smoke from the guns. I
saw the graves of my folks south and north having
known all along my ancestors had blessed the return
journey of a native son. I had known it. Think of me
standing in the valley of my childhood in the north,
fixed at the foot of the mountain where I had known
the terrors of the dark even when on summer nights it
was jubilee for myriad fireflies. Think of me standing
in the school house where I had learned to read and
speak. I seemed to hear the stampede of our herd as it
was with you when you remembered the village of
Dyilor except that you were shaken up by the
insidious European silence.

Your words float back to me and I read your

meaning:

> Back in time to Dyilor, back on the nurse's knees,
> remembering her stories, recalling the royal drums. The
> griots[6] sing their epics once again on their instruments. I
> can see my father lying on the mat, strong and beautiful.
> From out there in the distance the wind would bring
> with it those days the warm and pungent smells, the
> lowing of a hundred beasts.

I greet you Senghor I greet you!

Once you heard the doors of your soul bang in
the wind while you felt disanchored from yourself
from your mother's language from the wisdom of
your ancestors, from the music of your primal being.
This time on the earth of my own ancestors which I
scooped with my hands to feel the warmth of it bathe
my hands, I secured my door with a strand of wire to
stop it banging about in the wind — it had been
banging about so long I'd ceased to care until like
now, I wanted calm so I could listen. Yet I know the
wind will come again and start the rumpus with my
door and I will let it so I don't forget . . .

Which is why I'm not so sure that I would blame or
praise my ancestors if they did not turn coarse
because of hatred in their hearts. I myself must now
return, so I hear the drift of the current in your
poem:

> Back to the shrines. This time in flesh. I'm listening, my
> ancestors, listen also to my prayer, I shall be off again
> tomorrow back on the road of an envoy to Europe. For
> now, I'm here on the steps of the tall house. I am
> prostrate at your feet, my own still carrying mud from
> the bog of civilization. You my ancestors took so many

French insults, so much of their derision and contempt, restrictions and oblique remarks. Then you pulled away my Fathers, when you saw your over-trusting hearts had been abused. Blessed are you for never having let your hearts turn coarse because of your own hatred. I have made friends with Europeans, as you know, those champions of the intellect, obsessed with form . . .

Because even this day my ancestors walk on the killing ground on the farming lands assigned to white folks by decree that drove away my people by the hundred thousand. *Desecration here and desecration everywhere — who will atone! I hear the ancestors cry.*

    You and I and all should know by now the poetry of a prodigal imagination — take comfort that we've got to kill it lest it cover bigger ground and choke the native crop like those insatiable weeds . . .

    I know that you can with the power and means at your command aid the young along the route to greater freedom of the mind the nursery of the truest poetry.

    I greet you Senghor I greet you and hope that you'll accept my humble tribute, my apologies for replaying your music for myself and others.

September 1977

FOOTNOTES:

1.   Leopold Sédar Senghor (b. 1906). President of Senegal, world-famous poet who, together with Aimé Césaire,

the late Léon Damas and Birago Diop, launched a literary movement for which Césaire was to coin the name *Négritude*. Négritude has developed various meanings, according to the emphasis particular writers, artists and sociologists wanted to give it, since the decade of the 1930s when the concept was first formulated. These poets and others from the French colonies met as students in France and became concerned about their writing styles and themes which were derived from French literature, having themselves been assimilated into French culture.

Négritude came to mean primarily the essence of being black, the amalgam of African traditional values. The new poetry of the thirties and forties used African images and symbols. It was intensely lyrical, and sang of ancestral presences, of African ritual, of dance and tom-toms, of African laughter, of savannah and jungle, and so on.

Senghor saw négritude as a concept that takes in all negro peoples of the world, and he insisted that it was more the style than the theme that characterized it. There was, according to him, a 'negro-African style'. But he and other poets and scholars who embraced négritude were through it forging a weapon against Western cultural imperialism. They were through it elevating African consciousness and pride that could survive colonial arrogance.

2. Senghor was born in a village on the Atlantic coast called Joal-la-Portugaise.

3. The road to Europe, the road the ambassador must travel. Senghor was representative for Senegal in the French parliament, before independence.

4. A kind of xylophone popular in West Africa.

5. Title of a collection of Senghor's poems, published in 1945.

6.   The griot was a minstrel or singer who came from
      common folk. He was part of the household among
      freeborn families (those who were not born slaves in
      West Africa) and he sang the family's praises and history.
      He recited stories and was also an acrobat, a jester.